MW00571772

"A whirlpool of stories circle the center—a riveting cold case that happened in 1969. Honest and introspective, *Shibai: Remembering Jane Britton's Murder* recounts the case, and through it, explores the protagonist's incredulity surrounding a woman-friend's death. A mystery within a mystery, the story is written in the second person, the years of living with this unsolved death deftly handled, in trying to make sense of what had happened and who the murderer could be. Rather than being a hindrance or a vehicle of accusation, the *you* becomes a road of self-exploration, attendant to varying aspects of the murder, the shibai found in it, and in the writer's life itself. The honesty is disarming at times, sad and heart rending in others, the *you* a way to look at life's triumphs and failures, as well as a way to examine the murder and the protagonist's role. Even after sixty-four or so years, with incarceration still possible, and the many aspects of innocence or guilt by association, the shibai of friends and enemies, how the nuance of language is shaded in the interplay of peoples' guesses about what had happened, and finally, who the murderer had really been all along are all parts of this wonderful and unusual book. Read it!"

—Juliet Kono Lee, author of *Anshū* and other books.

"For fifty years, Don Mitchell lived with the memory of finding his friend and fellow anthropology classmate, Jane Britton, murdered in her apartment. Questioned then about his potential involvement, Mitchell struggled for decades with a lack of answers about her death. In his book, he explores how memory and meaning shapeshift, the way facts can shatter long-held perceptions about one's self and others, and how love and connection transcend time and culture. Mitchell's bare, poignant memoir about his life as an anthropologist, writer, and photographer circles again and again back to Jane and ends with a shocking resolution no one expected."

—Ronlyn Domingue, internationally published author of *The Mercy of Thin Air* and the *Keeper of Tales Trilogy*.

"In the early morning of January 7, 1969, Jane Britton, a gifted Harvard graduate student in archaeology, was murdered in her Cambridge apartment. Don Mitchell, a close friend who lived in the neighboring apartment, never heard a thing but found her body the next day. On one level, the book recounts Mitchell's compelling and brutally honest odyssey in dealing with this traumatic event for half a century until the murder was finally solved in November 2018. But on a deeper level Mitchell forces the reader to grapple with the passage of time, the nature of truth, indeed with life and death itself. And he takes us on a captivating cross cultural journey, moving from the remote Pacific island of Bougainville to the dramatic Mauna Kea volcano on Hawaii's Big Island to the bowels of the Cambridge police station. Mitchell's life took turns he never expected and he weaves a fascinating tale in seeking to make sense of it all."

—Michael Widmer, Journalist and former president, Massachusetts Taxpayers Foundation.

"Gritty investigative reportage becomes page-turning fiction in Don Mitchell's capable hands. Based on a real life and long unsolved killing that the author himself was for a time considered a suspect in, *Shibai: Remembering the Jane Britton Murder* is a breathless, globe-spanning mystery that also doubles as both a love story and a fascinating anthropological investigation into the human heart and mind. Fans of everyone from James Ellroy to Bill Bryson should race out to get themselves a copy of this terrific book."

— Sean Beaudoin, author of *Welcome Thieves*.

"In this compelling hybrid memoir and true-crime account, Mitchell recounts how the cold-case murder of his friend Jane Britton, a fellow graduate student in the Harvard anthropology department, was solved after 49 years. *Shibai*, a Japanese word for a stage play, also means "gaslighting" or "bullshit" in the slang of Mitchell's native Hawai'i. As an anthropologist among the Nagovisi people of Bougainville, Mitchell learned early that truth is always filtered through the stories we tell ourselves and the roles in which our culture casts us. When Becky Cooper, a journalist for *The New Yorker*, contacts him for a book she is writing about Jane's case, he discovers, in retelling the story to a stranger, that his long-held assumptions about the murder don't hold up. With him, the reader relives the Kafka-esque terror of being suspected by the police, the frustration when the investigation is stonewalled or misled by people he once loved, and the sorrow and relief of finally filling in the gaps about Jane's last moments. The resulting saga is a profound and subtle meditation on memory, aging, and our responsibility to the dead. Like a shadow that provides contrast in a photograph, Jane's unlived life stands as a counterpart to Mitchell's honest and self-aware journey through the milestones of his 70-

plus years, from the triumphs and disappointments of his academic career to his deep relationship with the Hawaiian landscape and people."

—Jendi Reiter, author of *Two Natures* and other books.

"With hypnotic and intimate language, Mitchell shares a deeply-personal story that spans decades and continents and explores the nature of self, of memory, of love, and most importantly of truth. In an age where reality itself is under attack, *Shibai: Remembering Jane Britton's Murder* reminds us that while facts are never subjective, the way we react to them can alter the course of our lives forever."

—Richard Cox, author of *House of the Rising Sun.*

"...really remarkable...a privilege to read. One because it feels very intimate and honest and two because it is such a finely told story, and three I love the many layers of thinking that are revealed: the how to tell a story and embedded demonstrations of such, the wrestling with what is real and what's shibai, what is others trying to understand your thinking, and what kind of thinking they want to lead you onto, and what is everyone's motivation for doing what they do, saying what they say."

—Ginia Loo, Ph.D., Punahou School.

# Shibai:
## Remembering Jane Britton's Murder

# Shibai:
## Remembering
## Jane Britton's
## Murder

## Don Mitchell

SADDLE ROAD PRESS

Shibai: Remembering Jane Britton's Murder
© 2020 Don Mitchell

Saddle Road Press
Ithaca, New York
saddleroadpress.com

Cover design by Ethan Mitchell

Cover photograph (Jane Britton, 1966) by Don Mitchell

Author photograph by Becky Cooper

ISBN 978-1-7329521-8-8
Library of Congress Control Number: 2020947774

Books by Don Mitchell
*A Red Woman Was Crying*
*Land and Agriculture in Nagovisi*

v1.3

*For Ruth and Becky*
*companions, champions, anchors,*

*and in loving memory of*
*Jane Britton*
*1945-1969*

Words came to her, so perfectly at the pace
of things they seemed not to move at all – and now
the odd details of her journey grew lucid,
the wilderness, at home in itself, made sense.
And telling it again made the same sense
again, made it deeper, gave it pleasure,
the water came up in the bucket clearer,
from a cooler, stiller depth of the well...

— Irving Feldman, "Ever After"

# CONTENTS

In Japanese culture, *shibai* refers to a "dramatic play."

In Hawaiian slang it refers to bullshitting, lying,
laying down a smokescreen, gaslighting.

# SHIBAI

THE PHONE RINGS.

Caller ID shows a 617 number, so you wonder if some troll from *The Boston Globe*'s website has found your phone number in Hawai'i.

It's been 48 years since your friend Jane was murdered, and your name and picture were splashed across the *Globe*'s pages.

It's been three days since the *Globe* published an article about Jane's murder and now, in Spring 2017, you're being savaged in the comments section. You told Todd Wallack, the journalist, how you'd kept the blood-stained goat-hair rug that her body was covered with, never imagining that readers would find this repulsive, even a sign that you were the killer.

So because you're pissed off and ready to tell any trolls to go fuck themselves, you pick up the phone.

It's a Massachusetts State Police detective—Sergeant Peter Sennott—and after he identifies himself you say, "This is about Jane, isn't it?" And you listen while he gets to the point, which is to ask if you'll submit to DNA testing. You don't speak for a moment, because you haven't forgotten how the cops tried to pin Jane's murder on you.

11

You haven't forgotten what leaked out of the Grand Jury room.

But a DNA test can exclude you, can put it all to rest, so it's worth it. And a refusal would draw suspicion to you again. And you don't want to risk that. Maybe your "Of course" surprises him, maybe not. He doesn't let on.

What happened 48 years ago went something like this. Early on the morning of January 7th, 1969, in Cambridge, Massachusetts, someone struck Jane Sanders Britton in the forehead with a sharp object, probably rendering her unconscious, then carried or dragged her to her bed and, using that tool or something else, smashed in the left occipital portion of her skull, killing her. Covered her up with a goat-hair rug and a coat. Threw red ochre over her. Left.

Asleep in your apartment next door you heard nothing. Around noon, Jane's boyfriend, a fellow Harvard graduate student, knocked on your door. "Jane missed her exam. I went in. Something's wrong," he said, so you walked down the short hall to her apartment with him.

And Jane's murder closed around you. Over the years, it sometimes held you tightly, sometimes loosely, but it didn't let go for half a century.

For the next month, you and your first wife Jill Nash endured not just the loss of a close friend, but the attentions of the police, ravenous media, an unsupportive Harvard Anthropology Department, polygraphs, and, finally, a Grand Jury with a leak.

Two months later you left Cambridge to begin anthropological fieldwork on a Southwestern Pacific island called Bougainville, among a people called the Nagovisi. You lived with them, on and off, for the next five years. They've been a part of your life, and you of theirs, for more than fifty years. What they taught you, and information you gathered on your own, have yielded an academic book and some articles, some published poetry and some fiction. Sometimes the creative has gotten tangled up with the science, but never by accident.

In Spring 2017, Jane's murder closed around you again. In the four years since you'd moved back to your childhood home in Hilo, Hawai'i, your life had fallen into a pleasant pattern: you laughed and worked with your partner Ruth Thompson, a poet; wrote fiction, designed books for small publishers; sold photographs; spent as much time as you could in the high back country of Hawai'i Island; and took twenty and thirty, even more than forty mile walks.

Then, suddenly, there were people clamoring for your attention, and very old memories became important in ways they never had been. Over the years you'd rarely had to retrieve them and talk about them, and then only with friends who knew nothing about the case.

These people were Todd, Becky Cooper (a former *The New Yorker* staffer working on a book about the case) and Sgt. Sennott. Todd's article was less about the murder than about how the Suffolk County DA had refused multiple Freedom of Information Act requests for the case files. Becky's project focused on the murder but also the Harvard anthropology community, Jane herself, and the ways in which her story had evolved. Sgt. Sennott was—well, you weren't sure what he was, or what he was really up to.

After getting off the phone, you immediately email Todd to tell him. He returns a link to a story on a Boston TV station featuring District Attorney Ryan, Todd, Michael Widmer (a former journalist whose first assignment as a cub reporter was Jane's murder) and, offstage, Becky and a young Colorado woman, Alyssa Bertetto, who had become interested in the case and was investigating it on her own.

DA Ryan seems uncomfortable and defensive. She can't honor the FOIA request because the case is active. They're doing DNA work, she says.

*That's me*, you think.

Then your stomach tightens.

*They're trying again.*

# FEARING

ONCE, NEWLY ON BOUGAINVILLE, you wanted to cross a stream waist-deep in flood, but your companions said "Absolutely not." The danger, they told you, was not the rushing brown water itself, but what was likely hidden in it: branches that would knock you down, would tangle you, and you'd drown. "What you *can* see isn't what's dangerous," they said. This happened not long after Jane's death.

Once a giant poisonous Bougainville spider left the forest, came into the village and spun its web over your back doorway while you slept. When you went outside in the night to piss you stepped into the big tough web with the spider racing around, shouted in terror, and killed it. In the morning, your woman friend Siuwako said "It came because it knew you feared it." This too happened not long after Jane was killed.

Once you were with some friends in the Papuan hills, territory of the deadly Taipan snake, easing along a trail none of you knew. In the lead by chance, you kept a sharp eye out for movement. Don't bother the snake and it won't bother you. Then someone said that the Taipan was aggressive and fast-moving and even if you flee it might chase and strike you from behind, killing you. The lesson you drew was that sometimes ordinary caution isn't enough. This was four years after Jane was killed.

Once, although you hadn't intended it, you challenged a killer tsunami and escaped. But the terror of cold salt water rising to your waist as you clung to a bridge and screamed has never left you, nor has the feel of the cold skin of the dead woman you pulled from the wreckage of her house a few hours later. You were sixteen years old. This was nine years before you put your hand on Jane's cold neck, and knew she was dead.

Now you're old, living in Hawai'i, in the house you grew up in, every part of it familiar. There are no deadly snakes, no poisonous spiders, and you don't have to ford any rivers to get home. There hasn't been a killer tsunami for almost sixty years.

You feel grounded and safe even when you're high on the dormant volcano Mauna Kea above the tree line, on foot, alone. Exposed. You don't personalize the dangers up there, the altitude and wind and cold and rocks. You respect them, but you don't fear them. They aren't out to get you.

But after the phone call you wonder whether the cops might be.

You remind yourself, *I didn't kill Jane.*

The fear says, *It's not that simple.*
The fear says, *They're trying again.*
The fear says, *They're going to trick you.*
The fear says, *You don't know how to protect yourself.*

## At the Police Station

January, 1969. You agreed to go to the Cambridge Police Station and talk to the detectives. This was maybe an hour after you'd found Jane's body. Her head had been covered by the rug, so you hadn't seen the wound that killed her. And you hadn't seen her face. You put your hand on her leg behind her knee where there should have been a pulse and it was cold. Then, even though you *knew*, you pulled down the rug, exposed her head, put your hand on her neck, and it was cold too. And there was blood.

It was as if she'd lain down on the bed and then covered herself up. Leaving her legs out, and spread apart. You remember the thought that flashed across your mind: *I shouldn't be seeing this* because in that first moment all you were aware of was that what was exposed was a private place, and if she were only sick or unconscious, you'd remember it and that would change the way you looked at her.

What you truly *shouldn't have seen* was the dead body of your friend, not her sexual parts.

After you understood she was dead, your first thought was that she'd killed herself. Over the years you've largely kept this to yourself, because out of context it seems ridiculous. Insane. You thought *suicide* because, only eight years before, when you were a freshman at Stanford, a kid in another dorm attempted suicide by cutting his throat the night before the first big freshman exam. You, and surely hundreds of other freshmen, were nervous, uncertain; had no very good idea what your first college exam would be like, or whether you'd prepared properly for it.

It hadn't been the suicide attempt that impressed you; it was the method. By then you had slit your own share of throats, but they'd been throats of ungulates you'd hunted down and killed. Not your own.

Jane had been saying for weeks that she wasn't prepared for her comprehensive exam. You had dismissed this, but suddenly, as you stood over her dead body, her blood on your right hand, on the day she'd missed her comps, you remembered that boy.

You knew something was very wrong and that you should not pull back the covers any farther, so you didn't, but you weren't thinking that she'd been murdered.

First you called the police. Then you called her father's office at Radcliffe, which was nearby, but he wasn't there so you told the receptionist to find him quickly and tell him "something bad has happened to Jane." When he got the message he was at lunch in Harvard Square with Jane's mother. They came rushing up the stairs, but the police were already there; you were standing guard outside her door and you had to tell them she was dead and they weren't allowed in the apartment.

They lost control of some of their bodily functions: gasping, belching. Sobbing. You had never been near anyone of any age when they were hit with anything like that, much less having been the person to tell them. They took refuge in your apartment. You can't remember what happened to them after that.

Forty-eight years later you found yourself in an interview room telling Sgt. Sennott that after you realized Jane was dead you remember nothing at all about what her boyfriend did, nothing about what Jill did. You remember the phone, the operator—because this was before 9-1-1—and you remember hearing yourself say who you were, where you were, and that someone had died, as if you were in a film. As if it weren't real and you were playing a part. Sgt. Sennott told you this was normal. "It's a kind of tunnel vision," he said, "it's common."

You were aware of passing into the same mode during the tsunami, after your near-death experience on the bridge, when you made your way back to where your teenage Rescue Squad was assembling, and set about rescuing dead bodies. No one your team found was alive, but you were careful, even methodical, in your search. You did not show emotion, particularly sadness or grief. You did not give in to your inner desire to scream "What the hell's happened here?" You thought simple thoughts. First do this, then do that. Pick up the body. Find transport to the hospital with its morgue. Leave it. Go back for more.

Soon a police car took you and Jill to the station.

Before the detectives began interviewing you, you'd had a chance to reconsider your suicide idea. Your first question was "Was it homicide?" and you remember choosing that over "murder." You remember the detective seemed surprised but quickly answered "Yes," and gave you a *Why are you asking such a thing?* look. You explained. You said that you'd "known somebody who cut his throat before an exam," but part of that was untrue. You hadn't known the kid at all.

So it was an hour or longer before you understood that Jane had been killed. Murdered. Your memory is unclear but you might have felt a kind of relief that she had not killed herself. And yet—what a strange relief. She was dead, murdered. No relief there but a kind of comforting certainty perhaps: she had not died because of *this*; instead, she died because of *that*, even though you had no idea at all what chasing down *that* would mean, what it implied, and you never thought nearly half a century would pass before you learned what *that* was.

But you were still in control of yourself. Still behaving calmly. Every muscle tight, though. Tensed against the unknown. You have no memory at all of what Jill was doing or saying to you. Perhaps they'd already separated you. Tunnel vision.

Then you entered the world of interrogation. The world in which people appeared to believe you'd done something you hadn't.

You agreed to have a detective treat your hands with a chemical and they shone blue, meaning blood, but of course they would because you'd touched her. They knew that.

Later you were present when they asked Jill why her hands had also shown blue, considering that she hadn't touched the body. "I have my period," she said, and then "Also I was handling London Broil."

"What's London Broil?" one of the detectives asked, and one of you answered it was a cheap cut of meat, and that the two of you and Jane regularly stocked up on cheap meat at the Waltham Meat Market. You remember thinking, *Why are we talking about cuts of meat and the cheap meat market here in a room at the police station when Jane's been killed?* You probably didn't think that as a complete sentence; it was a feeling. You probably didn't think *This is surreal* but that was how it felt to you.

You hadn't been in the hands of the police since you were detained one Sunday back in 1962 in Craig, Colorado for a motorcycle muffler violation, and those cops had been gentle with you, a college student riding alone, who didn't have enough cash to pay the fine. They told you they'd be locking you up until the judge came in Monday morning, but then one of them told you how you could use your gas credit card to pay the fine and be on your way.

This was different. In Cambridge you had no idea how to behave. What to worry about. Whether you should protect yourself...but against what? You'd done nothing. So you stayed in careful mode, observant mode, hold-it-in mode, even though you were coming out of shock and into grief.

You agreed to be interviewed, and to have it recorded. They walked you through those first minutes after the boyfriend knocked on your door.

Forty-nine years later you saw those early records, the notes, the reports, though not the interview transcripts. They were shockingly inconsistent with one another. The responding officer wrote one thing; the first detective on the scene wrote another. It was hard to see how you and Jill and the boyfriend could have been inconsistent: it was after all a simple thing to tell—you entered the apartment, saw her lying on her bed, head and torso covered up, you went to her head—oh, wait, you touched her leg, behind the knee, feeling for warmth and not finding it?—reached under the covering, felt cold skin, came away with blood, called the police. Simple enough.

But in 2018 it was a reminder: written records can be as inconsistent as memory. The world likes to think of them as *real*, as *facts*, but that's not necessarily so.

Then, after all of that, you walked out of the station into a world of movie cameras, big Speed Graphic press cameras with their flashbulbs, mics that were stuck in your face, a shouting commotion unlike anything you'd ever experienced. You thought *I'm that guy I see on TV.*

Someone took you back to your apartment. One of the papers said it was "a friend." You have no idea who it was. You have no idea whether you ate dinner. You don't remember drinking, but it's hard to imagine you didn't. You don't know what you and Jill talked about. You do know that you didn't hug or touch. You seem to remember keeping your distance, and if that's not a false memory it's at least a consistent one. You were still in that state of exaggerated calm. You wanted some space around you.

# SERVICES

A DAY OR TWO LATER, Jane's mother called and asked you and Jill to go into Jane's apartment, and select the clothes in which she would be dressed for burial. She gave no guidance. Opening dresser drawers, you and Jill looked at each other and because you supposed Jane should be decently clad for burial she selected a bra and looked for a pair of underpants. "I can't find any that aren't stained," she said. There was nothing to be done. You barely held back tears while rummaging in another drawer looking for a slip. Stockings. Dress and shoes from the closet.

The stains' raw intimacy broke your heart.

The Brittons invited you and Jill to sit with them at the funeral. Before the service, you were photographed with the Cambridge PD's photographer, who was holding a 16mm movie camera, filming the crowd. You remembered nothing about that until, in 2020, Becky Cooper showed you the picture.

You do remember what Jill's sister told you she heard in the church when you and Jill walked in: "There are the Mitchells. I know they did it."

23

You don't remember how it happened that you parked your car directly across the street from the church entrance. You do remember that, because it was a cold day, there was condensation on the driver's side window. Jane's coffin was being put into the hearse. You did what you normally did, which was to start wiping it off with your gloved hand. "Stop," Jill said, "it looks as though you're waving at her." She was right; it did, and over the years every time you've thought of that innocent slip you've felt ashamed.

The burial was private, but there was a gathering at the Britton house after. It seems to you that the mourners were at the house before the burial party returned, and so, once again, you were at a place where Jane lived when her parents walked in, grieving.

You never went to the grave, but in May 2018 Becky did, and asked you if you wanted anything brought to it on your behalf. You wrote,

> I don't believe in an afterlife or a spirit world but I certainly believe in the power of personal ritual both to make the living feel better, and to clarify their thinking. Will you please stand there and say to Jane that I've never forgotten her and never will, and that she remains alive in my memories? If I'm wrong about the spirit world, that ought to please her. No matter what, it'll please me.

In 1995, as an exercise, you wrote four short poems about death. One was about Admiral Yamamoto's death on Bougainville, one was about a Nagovisi woman killed by an American fighter plane, one was about a sandbar in a Bougainville river carpeted with dead blue-winged butterflies, and one was about Jane.

> Your forehead's crescent wound
> is redder than your lips. You had no time
> to make up for death.

## Being Sweated

January, 1969. You were naive. You saw no need for a lawyer. You'd heard of a case called Miranda, so at one point you asked the detectives if they weren't supposed to read you your rights. One of them laughed and said it wasn't necessary because you hadn't been taken into custody. You were at the station of your own free will.

Sometimes in the night or sitting in your apartment looking out at the Charles River or taking the T to yet another interview you were frightened. How could you prove to them that you hadn't killed Jane? You had no alibi. You and Jill were the last ones known to have seen her alive. Only Jill could account for your whereabouts that night, and you for hers, and the way you understood it, married couples couldn't alibi each other.

You've never forgotten that. Over the years it's become almost a game: you're alone somewhere, and you ask yourself how you could prove you were there, and not somewhere else. Most of the time, you see a way. Sometimes you can't, and you realize that if you were accused of being somewhere you weren't, doing something you hadn't, that you would have no defense except to assert that you weren't, that you hadn't. And even after all the years, you remember that feeling of dread when you

realized you couldn't prove you hadn't done something.
You could only hope they couldn't somehow prove you
had, by lying.

The Massachusetts State Police asked you to come
downtown and talk to them. You and three or four of
them were all seated at a table, as if in a meeting. One
of the detectives casually picked up a manila envelope,
opened it, and slid over to you an eight by ten glossy of
Jane's flayed skull, left occipital crushed, saying, "Did
you do this?"

You'd seen your share of skulls at the Department,
but you'd never seen the skull of someone you loved,
skinned of its thick dark hair, with what seemed to be
small bits of flesh still attached. Flaps of skin on the
stainless steel autopsy table.

*My god they cut her head off,* you thought.

It was so shocking you couldn't speak for a moment.
You shook your head.

"No," you finally said, "I didn't do that," but you
knew they were thinking *Maybe you did.*

Even now you don't forgive them the flayed skull.

There was a bloody fingerprint on Jane's kitchen
windowpane. A Cambridge detective, somehow
knowing you did photography, asked you if you'd
photograph and print it, so they could run it. You took
your tripod, focusing rail, Nikon F with macro lens over
to Jane's, shot the print, and the detective went with
you to your darkroom, which was in another part of
Cambridge, in a professor's basement. You also shot
some Ektachrome slide film for them; the detective took
it. "Chain of custody," he said; you hadn't heard that
expression before.

You developed the film and made some prints. On the wall next to the enlarger were two prints from a high-contrast high-grain session you'd done with Jane and Jill. The prints were flawed, but you liked them so they went up on the wall. The detective was interested in them, not surprisingly.

At about that point you starting wondering whether the whole photography business was an elaborate ruse to get into your darkroom, for…for what? Perhaps to find evidence that you and Jane were romantically-linked? What about the picture of Jill, then? You remember giving the detective the Jane print, along with the still-damp ones of the fingerprint.

The Cambridge cops liked to arrive unannounced. When the dicks knocked on the door and said "We just thought we'd have a talk with you," or "We thought of a few things we'd like to ask you," you didn't say to yourself, *Uh oh*. You said, "OK, sure."

Once there were three of them. They backed you into a corner and menaced you. "You were fucking her. You were fucking her. We know you were fucking her."

You looked from one to the other and they all had on different faces. One was shaking his head, as if to say *Why don't you just admit it*, one was nodding his head, as if to say *Come on, get it out*, and one was expressionless. They were all looking at you, and you knew they were looking for signs…signs of what? Lying? You weren't lying. Shading the truth? You weren't. You hadn't been fucking Jane; you hadn't been doing *any* sexual acts with her.

All you could say was "No, no, no." You were afraid that somehow they'd make you say what you were thinking: *But I thought about it. But I would have if she'd asked.*

The denials they forced from you dragged your friendship with Jane into cop-swamp filth, fouling it. You don't think you'll ever forget those moments.

Their theory of the crime, you later heard, was that you were having an affair with Jane and had killed her when she threatened to tell Jill.

Over the years you've come to understand that what they put you through was *nothing* compared to what other suspects endured in other rooms, other years, with other cops. But, an innocent, you didn't know that then. You got off easy, but at the time you didn't know that either.

The polygraph sessions were more sedate. Oh, those innocuous first questions. "Do you live at 6 University Road?" "Are you a graduate student at Harvard?" "Yes" or "No" were the only answers allowed. You cleared the first round and thought it was over, but they brought in a hired gun from Chicago for a second round. He had a good one: "Do you believe in God?"

You answered "No."

When he asked "Did you have a sexual relationship with Jane?" you answered "No," and wondered if you'd spiked any needles because of *But I wanted to.*

The final question was of course "Did you kill Jane Britton?" and you answered with a strong "No."

Afterward you asked him about the God question. He said, "I use a 'No' response as my ambiguous baseline because nobody's certain about that."

You'd been certain about that for years. If he took your definite God *No* as ambiguous then probably your sex *No* and your killing *No* registered as ambiguous, which could be dangerous.

You should have gone with Pascal and bet on God's existence.

# You Decide to Write in Second Person

THIS ISN'T THE FIRST long piece you've written in second person.

In 2003, just after your mother died, you were in Hilo with your third wife Mary Richert. One day, you decided to clean up a long-neglected part of the one-acre yard and so you took up your long Crocodile brand machete, sharpened it, and got to work. It was hard, but while you were at it the rhythm of your cutting strokes led you to weave together a handful of strands including what you'd seen on the web that morning, namely that a Solomon Islands warlord named Harold Keke had killed six Anglican brothers, which gave you one strand.

Then, because of the killing, you began thinking about a Nagovisi man, Mesiamo, whom you had truly loved and who had been your teacher but was himself a killer who spent hours telling you about his violent past. That gave you another.

You thought about your recent return to the village and what you saw and felt and brought back with you.

And you thought about your mother, so recently dead at almost 98, and how you had not been with her when she died.

And you thought about how easily you'd fallen back into the rhythm of cutting bush, something the Nagovisi had taught you to do years before.

And you were slashing an exotic jasmine called Queen of the Night, which had made you wheeze when you were a boy. At night, lying with Mary in your mother's bedroom, you sank into its heavy perfume.

Mary was not on your mind when you were slashing and clearing; you hadn't wanted her to join you, because you wanted to do the things you needed to do in Hilo by yourself. You knew you'd have to leave her; in not much more than a year you'd be divorced.

After you showered you went immediately to your computer, where you typed "You're slashing Hawaiian vegetation with a 'Crocodile' machete, the brand Solomon Islanders call *pukpuk*, and it's all coming back to you."

Second person simply came upon you.

That opening line stayed with the piece through all its permutations, including a multi-media performance in Buffalo, when it was billed as "Queen of the Night," finally making its way to YouTube. Its final print home was as the last chapter in your book of short fiction, in which the anthropologist very loosely based on you finally got a voice. All the other narrators were Nagovisi telling stories about him, the *Other* who had come to live with them.

Someone asked you why you'd chosen second person, and you answered that it seemed to have chosen you, which was too facile, so you added "because I like the distance and uncertainty it gives." Part of the uncertainty in that final chapter is whether the narrator is the fictional anthropologist, or you. You mixed it up, wove together all those strands, some true and some not true.

You wanted your readers to end with a sense of uncertainty: to wonder whether you lied when you said the anthropologist was not you. But your intent was never to trick them.

And so has it been with this book, which had its genesis in an hour-long audio recording you made while driving over the Saddle from Hilo to Waimea one day for a meeting, when you were troubled about what might happen when Sgt. Sennott arrived to take your DNA.

It's Saturday the 8th of July. Heading for Waimea.

This morning I got the idea of writing a nonfiction piece about what's been happening in the last week or two weeks and then perhaps earlier than that.

Talking about writing a novel and then about how parts of the novel get real.

So when I started thinking about the piece and how it might go, I realized it's gotta have everybody in it, because the people that I've been talking to about this are all people with whom I have different sets of relationships.

There's Ruth, whose relationship with me is intimate, she knows what I think, I know what she thinks, there's nothing we don't talk about and I have complete and utter trust in her.

Becky, also goes without saying. Becky would be interestingly difficult to work in, because I wouldn't want to compromise anything that she will write. So I don't want to undercut her but she has to be there, because she's been a part of this whole thing for what, two months now?

She became a part of it because my phone rang and I answered it. So we are on interestingly parallel slash not parallel tracks where she is writing non fiction about something that I'm writing fiction about.

About six weeks later—August 23, 2017, to be precise—you opened up a document and typed "You look over at the phone and see a 617 area code."

And here you are in Fall 2020, still in second person.

# PRONOUNS

IN ENGLISH, "you" is both singular and plural. But in the Nagovisi language that you and Jill learned to speak out in the Bougainville rainforest only a few months after Jane was murdered, pronouns are more precise: all pronouns distinguish between one, exactly two, and many individuals.

In this book written in English, your reader's going to have to depend on context or make a guess how many people you're talking about.

Had you been writing this in Nagovisi, you'd have been able to completely remove the *you*-ambiguity that plagues this story in English by using the second-person-dual pronoun (*le*) when referring to you and Jill, or you and Jane, and the second-person-singular (*li*) when referring to yourself in the way you are here, and of course for all those reading what you've written (provided there are more than two of them) you can use the second-person-many (*lii*), or more precisely second-person-three-or-more.

And because Nagovisi further distinguishes pronouns according to kin relationships, which is why they have 63 pronouns, you could have used the pronoun that denotes *two-people-who-are-married* for you and Jill, and the one

35

that denotes *two-people-who-are-not-kin* for you and Becky. The Nagovisi pronoun system doesn't encode "friend" or "collaborator" or, for that matter, "interrogator."

You realize you don't know whether the husband-wife pronoun changes after a divorce, because you and Jill divorced many years ago, well after you left Nagovisi. Writing about the past, in the present, do you use *pronoun-that-was* or *pronoun-that-is*?

Writing this, you realize you had better explain why you're talking not just about pronouns but about a complex 63-pronoun language, and a culture way the hell out in a recently war-torn Pacific island, in a book about your friend's murder almost half a century before.

It's because of the way that culture has worked itself into you, changed you, modified the ways you see other people and how you believe they should be treated. And that colors what you write, whether it's fiction about them, fiction about Jane, or a memoir about something that happened years ago that's affected you in the present.

Even when you were a practicing academic anthropologist you never thought, never claimed, that what you wrote was "correct." When you published your monograph on land and agriculture—in which you questioned conventional wisdom about cash cropping and development—you quoted the radical French economist René Dumont: "...if I arrive at honesty and objectivity, which is very difficult, I am pleased." As you hope you'll manage here.

You never—not even when you were a beginning photographer—bought into the vulgar *I am a camera* trope. Nobody's a camera even when their eye is glued to the eyepiece and their hands focus and adjust exposure without conscious thought. The way you framed that picture has something to do with who you are. So does the way you exposed it and processed it and this was as true back in the days of developing and printing film in a darkroom as it is in these days of Adobe Lightroom.

This is not the same as asserting that everything is subjective. It's merely an acceptance that human beings see, remember, forget, narrate, are mistaken, and even lie according to who they are and what they've learned. In what culture they were raised and learned how to be. To an anthropologist, nothing could be more obvious.

So if you're going to write about Jane and Becky and Sgt. Sennott and the others, you'll need to bring Nagovisi into it as much as Hilo, Palo Alto and Stanford, Cambridge and Harvard and what you saw and learned in those places. And you've been writing fiction in which both Jane and her killer and your fictional anthropologist and the sorcerer-killer Mesiamo appear. And they belong even in non-fiction. They are a part of you.

Anthropologists are aware that their presence in a community causes ripples in social space-time, and try to minimize these ripples. But you don't know of any apart from yourself who talks—writes—openly about how *they* and *their culture* affected *you*. The Nagovisi taught you ways of being in the world—being with other people—that changed you and have stayed with you all these years.

It's not as though they turned you into one of them. But you know a lot about how they see things, how they think people ought to treat one another, and these ideas have become a part of you. There's no mystery. It's called paying attention. It's called internalizing.

All cultures change, so you can't be sure how much of what you internalized back in the late sixties and early seventies has changed by 2020. When you returned in

2001 you were aware of material culture change, of linguistic change, certainly of political change, but it did seem to you that the same basic principles were still in operation.

Here's what you made part of yourself, apart from acute pronoun sensitivity.

Even exchange. Balance. If a person gives another person something, or helps her, then she's obliged to reciprocate, but not necessarily return or help with the same thing. A person should never attempt to dominate another by giving more than can possibly be returned, nor should a person try to shame another into giving more than is owed. Avoiding direct competition is a virtue. The balancing doesn't have to happen immediately. Lineages and clans will balance their exchanges in the long run— which might take a generation or two.

In consequence, the Nagovisi were egalitarian to a fault. Other Bougainvillean cultures were competitive, some intensely so. Your advisor had worked in one of the competitive ones—the Siwai—only thirty miles from the Nagovisi. Siwai held the Nagovisi in contempt, as ineffectual losers. The Nagovisi held Siwai in contempt as overbearing, greedy, and thoughtless.

Much later in life you wondered whether the differences between the cultures the two of you studied could partly explain your middling anthropological career and your advisor's Major Figure one. You thought it possible.

# You Feel the Need of Some Danger

Buffalo, late 2000. Thirty-two years after Jane was killed.

You've been living in Buffalo and teaching at the local four-year state college since you completed your Ph.D. and a post-doc at the Australian National University. You and Jill divorced in 1985. You foolishly remarried in 1988 and divorced again in 1994. Equally foolishly—maybe more so—you married yet again in 1997, and will divorce in 2004. Then you will find Ruth, your long-lost college girlfriend, and remain happily together, for sixteen years so far.

You were walking around Delaware Park one afternoon with Mary. You'd decided to go and see your Nagovisi friends on Bougainville, that island you left in 1973, four years after Jane was killed. In the intervening years you'd written a book about them—a technical monograph about tropical agriculture—and published a couple of poems, a personal essay, and some fiction in the only anthropological journal that published literary anthropology. You'd won two prizes from them for your writing. You'd had a story about Nagovisi nominated for a Pushcart by another literary magazine.

On Bougainville, a war of secession had been sputtering and flaring for more than a decade. The fighting had died down, although there were still crazy young men with automatic weapons putting up roadblocks, especially at the Panguna copper mine—which was what the fighting was largely about—through which you knew you'd have to pass. The Bougainville Revolutionary Army—the BRA—had its political wing, its dedicated military wing, and its unofficial crazy wing. The fighters you were likely to be stopped by belonged to the crazy wing.

You intended flying to the north part of the island, and then making your way to Nagovisi by land, through territory where you weren't known, and then into the teeth of the armed guys, who didn't much like white people. You knew it was going to be at least mildly dangerous, but you were reasonably sure that you could keep any crazy wing guys from killing you because, as you laid out to Mary, you could speak the *lingua franca* fluently, you could still speak at least halting Nagovisi, and you knew a few words of Nasioi, the language of most of the crazies.

So if they were to point their M-16s at you, you'd be able to speak to them in a language not English, and they should relax and you could negotiate with them. Plus surely they would be surprised and pleased by the white man who spoke one of the island's fourteen languages.

Finally, you told Mary, there's a man named Mesiamo. Even dead a quarter-century, his name's a powerful one and you can claim a close relationship with him, the much-feared killer and alleged sorcerer who was one of your teachers. You feel certain that if you say you're Mesiamo's clan-mate, his student—both of which are true—that will help.

"I guess," Mary said, "I still don't understand why you want to go."

"Because I feel the need of some danger." It just popped out.

You'd been living among Mary's friends, and you'd learned that you were the guy whose activities were not found interesting. To them you were *Mary's husband*. To them, you were lucky to have married their friend, as if you'd married above your station. And so this thing about the need for danger, the thing that just popped out of your mouth, had a component of *I do things none of you can even imagine doing.*

That wasn't a very good reason, but there it was.

You didn't bother trying to talk about this with Mary. You knew she was incapable of understanding it.

On Bougainville, Wakai—the truck driver—planned to pass through the roadblock at midnight, when the fighters would be drunk or sleeping. Indeed no one was manning the gate, and because Wakai had a sense of humor he stopped the Toyota at the roadblock and everybody got out and pissed on the gate.

No need for your languages, no need for your kinship, no need for Mesiamo.

The only terrifying part that night was getting the Toyota across a bridge that had been damaged in the fighting. Wakai nursed his truck along a series of planks laid end to end across the bare supports. Fifty feet below, a rocky river. A man sat on the front bumper, lit by Wakai's flashlight and made hand gestures: a little bit to the right, a little bit to the left, straight ahead.

At the trailhead you and two villagers walked down the long trail into the village without incident. It was still familiar, even after 30 years. Even in the dark.

Before you got to the village you left the trail and went to where you knew Mesiamo had been buried. Your beliefs about the absence of an afterlife were the same as they always had been, but you felt the need of a ritual greeting—and also wanted to make the point that he was still important to you. You approached his grave and said, in his language, "Old One, I've returned."

Then you entered the village. Someone had gone ahead and awakened everyone. There was shouting: "Our white man has returned!" You stood under a house, lit by kerosene lamps, surrounded by villagers.

Only two of the people you dearly loved were still alive. One was a woman to whom you'd given the name Siuwako in your fiction. You had spent days, weeks, months working with her in her food gardens, learning, measuring, tracking. Her husband—now dead—had been your best young friend. You'd won a prize for a poem about your relationship with her.

You were anxious to see her. Anxious to rekindle... rekindle what? Not romantic love. Something else—a kind of quiet closeness you'd never experienced before with any woman before her, although perhaps with Jane. If there had been a sexual undercurrent it was a quiet, slow one.

More than once you realized you'd taken the role of younger sister, rather than as a man with whom she could have been sexual. You carried her little daughter everywhere.

All the years you were apart you believed she was the one who saw your true nature, just as you believed your long-lost college girlfriend Ruth had. You and Siuwako never talked about anything like that. No line— Nagovisi or anthropological—was ever crossed, or even

42

approached. But you knew what had happened. Was happening.

When Siuwako appeared out of the dark, smiling and excited, her first words to you were, "You're fat," because you were carrying a good twenty pounds more than the last time you saw her.

"True," you said, went to her, and shook her hand, because Nagovisi adults don't hug.

# How Not to Save Yourself

THE OTHER PERSON YOU LOVED was a man named Lalaga, who was one of the smartest people you've ever known. You spent hours talking with him, going over what had changed and what hadn't, what your life had been like, the same for his. One day the two of you were chewing betel nut and talking about the fighting. Lalaga told you about an attack in which some crazy BRA fighters had marched down from the mountains, threatened everybody, killed one man, stuffed his body down an outhouse, and gone back into the mountains.

You asked where they came from and he named a Nasioi village.

"Why were they angry at us?" you asked.

"Not at us, at Mesiamo."

"But he's been dead twenty-five years!"

"Because of Oni." Lalaga looked at you. You could tell he expected you to remember.

You spit red betel spit on the hard-packed earth. You sat there, trying. Oni, Oni. Oni! A Nasioi leader. It came back to you, although it had been thirty-one years since you wrote it down, and more than a half-century since it happened.

October 5th, 1970. Mesiamo was talking about Oni, and how Oni insulted him so Mesiamo humiliated him by beating him with a cane in front of many people.

You said to Lalaga, "But the fighters were probably the grandchildren of Oni's people!" and Lalaga slapped you on your thigh and said, "Have you forgotten what we're like?" You remembered Mesiamo's schooling you about *mude-mude*, a hidden anger that can last generations, so you said "Ah, *mude-mude*" and Lalaga answered, "That's it."

"Fuck a dog! If the BRA got me at Panguna I was going to link myself to Mesiamo and hope they'd respect me."

"For that, they might have killed you."

So there it was. What you'd thought would keep you out of danger was the very thing that would have catapulted you into it. Something you wore like a badge would have been a target. Perhaps they would have killed you.

Well, almost certainly not *killed*. Perhaps detained for a time.

You returned to Buffalo, where you did not tell Mary about Mesiamo, although you did tell her about going through the roadblock at midnight. She didn't say much. Later, you heard her announce to her friends that you'd had a nice trip, a good time, that you'd had fun.

You weren't surprised that she had no concept of what you'd been doing, because early in your marriage she'd said of your years of fieldwork, "Perpetual Club Med, right?"

# Counting

One, two, three.

One. The number of your friends who were murdered.

Two. The number of your friends who were killers.

Three. The number of wives you had before Ruth.

In English, you (that's the three-or-more you, *lii*) count everything in the same way, no matter what it is. "Three" is as appropriate for wives as it is for strikes in baseball, or the number of guesses you're allowed.

But that's not how it works in Nagovisi. There is no generic "one, two, three." Like pronouns, the Nagovisi counting system divides the world into many categories, in which each number has its own name. To count something properly, you have to know its counting class.

You intended to collect folk taxonomies, but when you started asking how they grouped birds, trees, streams and forests you got nowhere until your teachers—finally figuring out what you couldn't find a way to ask them—began telling you about counting classes. And there it was. Physical, social, intellectual, mythical, spiritual worlds categorized by how you count what's in them.

Some words for *one*:

> *Nabore.* One head, stone, betel nut…
>
> *Namai.* One stone adze, knife, axe, dog…
>
> *Namo.* One person, bird, possum…
>
> *Narusi.* One dirge, myth, prayer…
>
> *Naviku.* One idea, trail, thought…
>
> *Nane.* One leaf, thatching, palm frond…
>
> *Navēle.* One penis, betel pepper, arrow…
>
> *Navedo.* One vagina or named tract of land.
>
> *Naveimo.* One funeral pyre or shooting star.
>
> *Nawaali.* One fight.
>
> *Nalu.* One breast.
>
> *Namago.* One leg.
>
> *Name.* One bed.

How many people lay dead in Jane's apartment? *Namo,* one (person).

How many legs did you see when you entered Jane's apartment? *Kemagola,* two (legs).

How many coverings were placed on her? *Keneka,* two (pieces of thatching).

How many detectives shouted at you? *Wenalo,* three (people).

How better to count those detectives? *Wekago,* three (dicks).

How many machetes do you have in Ithaca? *Wemailagu,* three (knives).

Now, in 2020, you wonder how to count sadnesses. The dirge counters? No, a dirge is an act, not a thought. The idea counter? No, ideas aren't emotions. You go through your notes looking for emotion counters, but you can't find any.

Longing, hatred, anger, fear: you don't know how to count these things either. But you could ask your Nagovisi Facebook friends. You think about Simon Kenema, the Nagovisi man who has a Ph.D. in anthropology. You could email him. As an anthropologist, the question should interest him. But even though he's in his forties, he may be too young. When you were working there, he was an infant. Even that long ago, young people didn't know all the counting classes and, like you, made do with three or four. Much of it's probably lost by now, you think. The last time you were there, young people simply code-swapped in English numbers, avoiding their own counters entirely.

In 2009 Simon was studying in Scotland so you arranged for him to fly over to your son's wedding in New York and represent his Nagovisi clan. In 2017, after Becky and Sgt. Sennott made their visits, he came to Honolulu for a conference, and you flew him over to Hilo, and showed him around your island. You were familiar with the bush hospital where he'd been born, so you took him to the still-standing but repurposed hospital where you'd been born. It had become an adult daycare center, which you found either funny or sad, depending on your mood. You asked someone in the parking lot to take a picture of the two of you, and it made its electronic way back to the village, where it was admired.

You told him about Jane's murder, and he told you how his Port Moresby girlfriend had been murdered. He was in another town and on the phone with her when it happened, and could do nothing about it.

"In a way, I witnessed it," he said. He had told you about this in 2009, but you'd forgotten the phone part.

48

You two (*le*) talked and talked into the night.

He's the grandson of Mesiamo, one of your two murderous friends.

# Letting a Body Rot

You spent much of 2011 and 2012 writing a novel—*News of Elsewhere*—about Elliot Lyman, anthropologist, among the Nagovisi. He was, of course, a graduate student at Harvard. The novel grew to 300,000 words and you couldn't see how to cut it down, so you mined it for material and in 2013 published your story collection *A Red Woman Was Crying*.

In *News of Elsewhere* you used multiple first-person narrators, a style you'd long admired, and in which you felt comfortable. In *Red Woman*, Elliot never narrated, but in *News of Elsewhere* he took his turn with the others. At first Elliot resembled you closely. But as is always the case, soon enough he shook you off and became his own man. Unlike you, he wasn't married. He had a radical girlfriend named Anna, who lived in Berkeley; she went underground to resist the Vietnam war. In *News of Elsewhere* the reader knows her only by her letters to Elliot.

Elliot lived in a village named Pomalate, as you had, and hung out with people very much like those you'd known—but not exactly and, like him, over time they increasingly diverged from their real counterparts.

In *News of Elsewhere,* an old man named Laumo dies, and his body's brought from where he lived (in his wife's village, as is customary) to his natal village. He had already been dead two days by the time he arrived, and in this excerpt he's been in the village another day. Although he's wrapped in blankets, he's rotting.

Elliot (like everyone else) has been enduring the smell as he goes around asking questions, making photographs, and taping the continuous mourning dirge. Because of the Catholic church, no one has been cremated in Nagovisi for many years. There's talk of cremating Laumo instead of burying him; Elliot knows that political and economic issues are swirling around the village, but no one will talk to him about them, just as no one appears to know whether Mesiamo, the leader, will call for Laumo's cremation.

In Nagovisi, a recently-dead person is referred to as "The Dead One," rather than by name.

> By afternoon Laumo's smell filled the village. I sank into the odor. What was to be done? Nothing. It wasn't as though there was a dead dog or pig that could be dragged away and buried. It was a rotting human corpse and the smell would only get worse until it was buried or cremated. And even Sunday afternoon no one would say which it would be.

> Mesiamo came over and sat for a while. He wasn't forthcoming, saying only that the decision would be made Sunday night and if he was cremated, it would happen Monday night. All Monday would be taken up preparing the pyre. I couldn't understand why he wouldn't tell me what he was going to do. At this point, I thought, what would it matter?

Mesiamo wanted to talk about the smell—did I mind it? I said "No," of course, and then I said, "A little."

"No one likes the smell of a rotting body," he said, "but it's essential. If The Dead One had been more important, we'd have kept him in the house for four or five days, and when that happens, the smell's very bad."

"It must be," I said, because I couldn't think of anything else to say.

"It's not only the smell," he said, "what people don't like is that the body weeps and liquids run out of it, and so you will sometimes see people digging little ditches to carry the fluids away, or perhaps throwing dirt under the house to cover it up."

I asked him why letting the body rot for so long was a sign of respect.

"You know the other things we do," he said. "We can't have fires, we can't eat cooked food, some people smear themselves with ashes and other people go into the bush and find bitter foods. No one can go to the garden to work, and not even to gather food. No one washes."

I was thinking I could jar him into telling me what he had in mind so I said, breaking protocol, "If I say what I think, will you be cross?"

"No," he said, "I'm always interested in what you think and I know that you're not supposed to talk about it. Go ahead."

I said, "The things I've learned about deaths, what people do, I think those are things that make the mourners not human, to become like the corpse, who is no longer human."

Mesiamo made a noise. "Go on."

"It looks to me like a way of saying to the dead person's spirit, 'Now we'll be just like you, doing nothing that makes us happy or makes us feel good or lets us overcome cold or hunger, and also by inhaling your stench we take you into us and share in what's happening to your body until we put you in the ground or burn you up.'"

He made a noise of approval. "Yes," he said, "that's a good way to talk about it. Those things are true and I'm glad you see that. But about the stinking, it's not as complicated as what you say. With the fires and bitter food and cold we are saying that we will turn away from what we normally do—eat good food, work, keep warm, stay clean, and we don't normally have stinking things around us. Therefore to set this mourning time apart from other times we *will* have a stinking thing around us and breathe its stink because in normal life, we don't."

I said, "Ah. I was also thinking of bad smell as invisible, like a person's spirit and so a person might say, 'There's an invisible spirit and an invisible smell and they go together, both are invisible.' But I see, as you say, I was making it too complicated."

Mesiamo said, "That's the kind of thing that Lalaga likes to talk about. I am not saying it's wrong but I am saying that there's no need to think like that because suffering and refusing to live normal lives are good enough reasons. This is what we do."

I said, "I'm not used to hearing you say "This is what we do" without a reason."

He laughed. "White Man," he said, "I understand what you're saying. But right now we have a dead man and we have to decide whether to cremate him or not, and there are things that people must do whether we cremate him or not, pigs to get ready, shell valuables, many things are happening and this is always the case when someone dies and at those times, what's important is for everybody to behave correctly. And although I never like being the person who *makes* people behave correctly, just now I am that person. Remember that no young people and not all the old people know how to put on a cremation."

I said, "But you do," and he said, "Yes, and you can see why I'm not thinking about any connection between smell and spirit. It's not something to think about now. Right now I have to do the leader's job."

"I understand," I said, and then I said, "I'm wondering how I'll know what you decide," and he said, "If men start bringing firewood to the village, that will tell you," and I said that I would wait and watch for that.

He got up as if to go, and then sat down again. "I'll send word to you before people go for the firewood. Only one kind of wood can be used, and the carriers must eat a certain food before going to get it. If they go and if you go with them to make photographs, you had better eat that food yourself."

I didn't think anything I said could influence him, but I said what I thought, "As long as I'm saying what I think, I'll say that I'm hoping you decide to cremate The Dead One because I would like to see that thing."

He made a dismissive motion with his hand, and said, "We'll talk about all of this later on. I don't think of you as an outsider any more, and so I'm telling you that you will know what will happen when the other people know it, not afterwards and not before. This is a difficult thing."

# Field Notes

You returned from your first field trip with about a thousand pages of typed notes. When interviewing you wrote in longhand, and then at night you typed the notes, making them a combination of research material and journal.

In 2008, you wrote "Outfielders," a story set in Nagovisi, in which Elliot's note-taking and processing didn't differ from yours.

> Elliot knows that holographic journals are as suspect as their transformations. Even as he writes live notes on his steno pad he's aware of constant filtering; writing as fast as he can, switching between two or three languages—whichever seems the fastest—he knows he's dropping things out, editing, condensing.
>
> Most days, usually at night by his lantern's red-shifted light, he types his field notes on a Hermes typewriter, clicking, thunk-shifting, the bell ringing, adding comments and thoughts that occur to him while he types, piling on another layer of interpretation, amplifying and distancing himself and the journal still farther from the events of the day.

When he goes to those pages twenty, thirty years in the future, confronting himself represented by himself, will he recognize the contortions of his *I*?

You searched your notes for mentions of Jane.

June 11, 1969. Listening to the Beatles album made me think of Jane and I became sad. I still think we should try to trap Lee Parsons [the person you believed was the killer] when we get back, whether he remembers having done it or not.

July 24, 1969. Back home again we thought what the hell and started to drink beer. No one was around anyway. I wrote to Lt. Joyce about the Jane thing.

September 30, 1969. I got up early in the morning, but I didn't notice them carry The Dead One back from Sovele, where he had died about 3 AM.

We didn't quite know what to do, so we went off for Wakoia, carrying notebooks and cameras. We ran into Tevu, who asked if I was going to take pictures. I said if they didn't want me to, I wouldn't. He said they didn't want me to. They were so sorry they didn't want anybody else around.

So we didn't go.

Well anyway it was very depressing. I kept thinking we should have just gone ahead over there; then I started thinking of all the people snooping and prying around when we were grief-stricken over Jane, and what we thought of them.

January 8, 1970. We passed the anniversary without incident. I had a dream of Jane about a few weeks ago, in which we talked quite naturally, at a party, and she kept referring to events before by saying, "Well yes that was before I got killed." But she didn't say who did it. It was like she was on a visit back, very strange, and it made me sad. Not dead, only gone away on a trip, like they tell little children.

## Running or Running Away?

At the end of 1973 you left Mesiamo and the others and returned to your research institute in Port Moresby, the capital. This was almost five years after Jane was killed. One of the other researchers said that people were doing a thing called "jogging," and would you like to join them? Off to the grass track at the University of Papua New Guinea you went, and that was the beginning of your running career.

At the time you didn't even know what a marathon was, but in less than three years you'd run your first one. About a year and a half after that, you'd break 3 hours and qualify for the Boston Marathon (where you ran 2:52, a decent time). You ran a string of mid-2:50 marathons ending with your last competitive marathon in 1981.

In 2003 you thought you'd try a 6-hour event, and managed 28 miles. After that, you started marathoning again, but much more slowly. You ran New York a couple of times, Buffalo once, but then after 2006, when you were 63, you let the long distances go for a few years.

But let's back up thirty years to when your ultra marathon career started.

In 1980 you entered a 50 mile race because you'd stupidly injured yourself just two weeks before the marathon in which you thought you could run around 2:48. You'd been in Delaware Park with a friend, doing *fartlek* (Swedish; "speed play")—accelerations, bursts of speed, running hard up hills, jogging. You felt your left calf tightening up after an all-out uphill leg of about a quarter mile, but kept going. It got worse. You kept going. Finally you stopped, but it was too late. You limped home, having killed your October marathon.

By December you'd healed, and thought about the Nickel City 50, which was being held in the Park. You'd laid out the course as a favor to the race director, who taught at your college.

The 50 attracted you, even though it was nearly twice as far as you'd ever run. There were a couple of experienced ultra guys entered, but most of the runners were marathoners trying an ultra for the first time. The course was multiple loops around Delaware Park. There were no aid stations; it was all self-service, although the race organizer put out some tables for individual drinks and food near the finish line. You laid out a large bottle of strong tea laced with honey.

About 35 miles out, you looked over your shoulder and glimpsed a runner you'd never beaten. By then you were feeling a little weird, not to say confused. You were learning that at some point in an ultra you stop thinking clearly. You assumed the guy was about to lap you. Being beaten was OK, but being lapped wasn't, so you speeded up. You looked back about a mile later and didn't see him, but you felt him back there, threatening you.

When you got to forty miles you felt good and said to yourself *Ten miles ain't shit* and picked up the pace, which was a mistake. You ran faster for another 3 or 4 miles, but after that you had to stop every lap and take a little walk. Even so, you took fourth overall.

After the race the guy you thought was lapping you told you that *you*'d actually lapped *him*, that when you went by he was in the bushes pissing, so you hadn't seen him. "I was trying to get unlapped," he said.

The Monday after the race you wrote your graduate school advisor—who had left Harvard for the University of Hawai'i and had run the Honolulu Marathon—about your success at the 50, and he was impressed and praised you by return mail. You ran Honolulu 35 years later, at 73, on the 40th anniversary of your first marathon. Someplace there's a file folder with his letter. Maybe, you think, you'll go find it and see which of you had the better time. You know which of you had the better academic career.

You do remember feeling unsettled. You were proud of your 50, but it was, after all, only running. Better he should have been praising you for something you'd published, or some academic award you'd gotten. You were aware that you had no academic successes to report. A top-five placing in ultramarathon was the best you could do.

You don't remember reflecting on it then. But looking back you can recover some of what you were feeling: unhappiness about how your life had unfolded, unhappiness in your marriage, unhappiness in your job, but your endurance abilities made up for it. No. Not *made up for it.* All they did was make you feel as though you could do a difficult thing and do it well. Do it better than any of your college friends or any of your grad school friends, or any of your post-doc friends in Australia and way better than your friends at Buffalo State College.

Sometimes you compared your academic life to your running life, but the comparisons inevitably fell apart. You hadn't managed to make any noise in anthropology, but you knew, or thought you knew, that your abilities were the equal of any of your grad school friends'. Where, then, had you gone wrong? Well, being at a four year college with no institutional support didn't help.

But it was more than that. It was *you*. You didn't have that fire in the belly. That competitive instinct. That drive to keep at it until you scored a paper in an important journal, or were invited to give a paper at an important conference. And you were distractible. If you happened on new path that seemed interesting, you followed it.

Or maybe it was the follow-through. You wrote a conference paper that you thought was excellent, and it was well-received. You published a version of it in a decent journal and you remember thinking, as you sat at your IBM Correcting Selectric, *I can't do any better than this…if this goes nowhere, I'll give up on anthropology.* It didn't, and you did.

The conference was in Galveston, Texas, in February. When making arrangements you'd learned that the Galveston Marathon would be run on a Saturday when you had no session to attend. You'd already qualified for the Boston Marathon in April, so you figured you'd do Galveston as a hard workout. You got up early, knocked off a 3:07 under cold, windy conditions, and got an age-group award.

Back at the conference hotel, you told a couple of people that you'd run a marathon that morning, but they weren't particularly interested. And why should they have been? You were there for intellectual reasons, not athletic ones. Were you showing off? You were. It was the good old *I can do what you do and I can do things you can't*. You know that feeling well, and when you inspect your life from as far back as you can remember, that's what let you feel good about yourself. In reflective moments you ask yourself whether that did anything for your career and your answer is always no.

You weren't very good at anything short. Your best mile in competition was 5:00.8 at an all-comers meet where you meant to break 5. The meet was running late, and although it was a summer night it was getting dark by the time the officials called for the "old man mile." The track (in fact the track at your college) had no lights, and so the organizers put everybody 20 and over in the same heat, instead of breaking it down. You knew who you expected be running with—the 30 and over guys, of whom there were at most ten. But with more than 20 runners on the track at once you couldn't get out at your own pace and you couldn't control it. You'd lost it by the second lap. Eight tenths of a second. The timer, who was a friend, showed you the stopwatch he was running on you. He said "Sorry."

You never took a shot at it again, and looking back you don't know why you didn't. The next time, you'd have gotten it. But it was time to start training for a fall marathon. You never ran in a track meet again.

Later in life—up until the time you began writing seriously—it had been always the same. Think you're ready for something, take your shot, get knocked back, give it up, go on to something else. An old story.

You remember how, when *The New York Times* reporter came to interview you and Jill, you'd said of Jane, "It is not possible to characterize her life style because she changed it so often. She was never taken in by any ethos, but she went through a period of painting on her wall, and then she would not do that, then it was music, and she would not do that." Looking at the clipping in 2020 it occurs to you that you weren't only describing Jane.

# Out There on the Net

In the 1990s and even as late as 2008 you'd been steadily publishing fiction and poety in an official American Anthropological Association journal called *Humanistic Anthropology*. They published everything you sent them, including, once, a draft of something you were working on that you sent to the editor for comments, and instead of commenting she replied "We want to publish this as is."

You first won their poetry prize, then you won their fiction prize, then you sat out about a decade before getting back in by co-winning their fiction prize.

You think of the last prize as something you won in anger. A Pacific anthropological listserve featured a couple of threads in which anthropologists were urging each other to enter (and, of course, win) the Society for Humanistic Anthropology's fiction prize. They were saying things along the lines of "It's easy to write...we can all write...one of us can win this," which angered you.

You remember pushing your chair back, going upstairs to Ruth's workroom, and saying, "Some ASAO assholes think they can win the fiction prize. So I will." You'd had a story in your head for a while, so you quickly wrote and submitted it, and shared the prize.

You hadn't published anything based on your own anthropological research since 1982, apart from a couple of multi-authored chapters in a book in which you were the lead author. And you were fine with that. Everything you now wanted to say about you and the Nagovisi you were saying in fiction.

In 2006 you shut down your timing business, after timing more than a million runners in more than a thousand races. You were sitting on a very large amount of performance data that you sometimes thought about mining. You'd tracked some of those runners for 25 years; for many, you had 10 and 15 year histories. In some kinds of research, longitudinal data are the gold standard, and that's what you had.

You saw an article in *The New York Times* about Robert Deaner, an evolutionary psychologist at a Michigan university who was working on male-female differences in competitiveness. You'd always been a little suspicious of evolutionary psychology as a discipline, because you thought it minimized the role of culture. But it was unquestionably legitimate. You emailed Deaner, offering your data, and he accepted. The two of you worked together, and in 2011 published a jointly-authored paper in the journal *Evolutionary Psychology*.

In December 2011 you and Deaner set yourselves up to answer questions about the article on the major US running website, letsrun.com. A poster who disagreed with your conclusions identified himself as a Harvard graduate. After some back and forth about how to prove a Harvard degree when online, the poster, who'd obviously done some quick googling, wrote: "Apparently you were involved in some sort of murder case as well."

You replied, "As for the murder, 'involved' is about right. It will have been 43 years in Jan 2012, and no one's been brought to justice. The most important person of interest died, but I keep hoping for something to turn up."

Three years later you were idly googling your book's title and your name, and were led to a cold case site called websleuths.com where a poster quoted what you'd said on the running site. You had no idea there was such a thing as cold case sites, much less one with a thread devoted to Jane's murder which had been running for two years.

You thought about what to do for two days, and then finally posted as yourself—no screen name—and spent the next four and a half years on the site, putting you on the path that led to *The Boston Globe*'s article, and Sgt. Sennott.

In January 2016, Jane's brother Boyd called you in Hilo and you talked for a long time. You'd tried to reach him over the years, but had always failed. You knew he was a Los Angeles radio personality, but not which one. Later in January, Boyd began posting on Websleuths.

Starting in June 2016, you exchanged private messages with a Websleuths member who asked you if you'd be willing to talk to the *Globe*. Soon you switched to regular email, beginning a series of exchanges that have lasted to the present. The writer, Alyssa Bertetto, was one of the people filing FOIA requests with the Suffolk County DA. She'd been investigating the case on her own from Colorado.

Alyssa hoped you could connect her with Jill. You tried, but Jill refused, writing

> I am rather tired of thinking about Jane's murder. [A friend] told me about web sleuths, which I guess you have joined, and when I read a bit on it, I was horrified by the rampant and ignorant and hurtful speculation by people who really need

to get lives. I now see Andrea occasionally and she has also been contacted by the ghoul class. It really hurts my feelings to see the relish with which people entertain themselves with talk about something that was a terrible and frightening event in my life.

*Well*, you thought, *so much for that*. But you had to try.

Later, you wrote to Becky that you thought Jill

…holds it, perhaps even cherishes it, as the thing it was, not the thing into which it's mutated over the years. And I doubt that she spends time thinking about how *she* has and has not changed over the years. She clings to frightening and terrible as fixed in January 1969 and I think a part of her believes that she owns the event.

You help Alyssa and Becky connect, and get out of the way.

You open up a channel with Todd.

## BECKY COOPER

APRIL, 2014. Someone named Becky Cooper calls and leaves a message. You return the call. She wants to talk about the Anthropology Department in the sixties. You don't remember how you sensed it might be about Jane, but you did. You remember being vague. In a subsequent email she said she had "a few specific questions that I'd prefer to ask you over the phone," which, to you, confirmed it was about Jane.

You replied,

> I'll say in advance that I don't want to talk much about Jane Britton's murder, and the reason is that although I don't think of life as a zero-sum game (not at all) I've been around the writing world long enough to know that sometimes writing is. After I finish the novel I'm working on, something fictional or a memoir about Jane is next up.

Then you wrote that you'd email her "when I see what looks like a good day."

You never did. You were feeling possessive; you didn't want to cooperate, so you put her off. From time to time over the next three years you remembered what you'd promised, and felt bad. You'd let her down. You started the Jane novel and kept working on it, although it wasn't going well.

April 2017. The phone rings. You see a 917 area code and, thinking it's your daughter-in-law, you pick up. It's Becky. She starts talking and you don't interrupt because you're ashamed of having blown her off. It turns out she's on staff at *The New Yorker*, which tells you she's no lightweight. You like the way she talks about her project. Soon you find yourself agreeing to meet her. Then agreeing to share everything you know. Then realizing there won't be any competition between her book and the one you're trying to write. *Why did I ever think that?* you ask yourself.

You and Becky begin exchanging emails and texts. You go through old letters and documents, scanning them, and sending PDFs to her. You haven't opened some of the folders for thirty or forty years. You talk about Lee Parsons, the archaeologist you believe killed Jane. About Cambridge. About the Peabody Museum. About the Anthropology Department (which is housed in the Museum).

At least once, looking at your folder of clippings, you remember how you and Jill were played by a reporter from a New York tabloid, who somehow—thinking back, you're not sure how—wormed his way into your confidence and then printed things you'd told him that you hadn't realized he might print. At that time, neither of you knew to declare "This is off the record." A betrayal.

Because of this, but only for a moment, you wondered whether Becky was playing you. At 74, you were no longer a young man ignorant of the ways of journalists, especially sleazy tabloid guys. You'd seen a thing or two, been around the proverbial block a time or two, knew a couple of newspaper reporters personally, and were confident you could spot any danger signals. There were none.

But you wondered how you'd do being interviewed by somebody with *The New Yorker* chops. You were perhaps overfond of referring to yourself as "an old white guy in the distant provinces" when trying to explain why your writing, especially your book, had not done well. When feeling depressed and uncertain you'd tell yourself that nobody's interested in what somebody like you has to say about anything. Yet it did seem clear that Becky was.

You and Ruth talk about whether to offer her your guest quarters. Before you decide, she tells you she's gotten an Air B&B. That makes everything simpler.

Becky comes to Hilo in April. You and Ruth pick her up at the airport. She's taller than you expected; you put a lei around her neck. When she offers her cheek for a kiss, you realize she's done her homework. She knows how things are done in Hawai'i. You already feel a strong connection from all those texts and emails, and her relaxed attitude confirms that you haven't misjudged her, or the situation.

The first Sunday, after you do your 28 mile walk, you text her, saying that you're not tired, and suggest you begin that afternoon. You drive down and pick her up; you live in the hills above town, and her Air B&B's down in the flats.

Ruth sits in the living room with the two of you, which is polite. You're getting to know each other. As you talk, you realize you're excited to be talking to a young woman from the big time, someone who's come to see *you*, and for whom learning who you are and what you know is actually the goal. Nothing like this has ever happened to you, and your response is to spill out much more than—you find out later—Ruth thinks you should have. You talk about how you didn't do much as an academic. You talk about your three marriages and how you finally found Ruth and for the first time are in a loving relationship with an equal. As Ruth puts it later, you let it all hang out.

You and Ruth take Becky to dinner where you always go on Sundays: Ken's House of Pancakes. It's a Hilo institution; you went to high school with the Sunday night hostess. She's still beautiful. Becky asks what a "loco moco" is, and you explain that it's a strange but popular dish invented in Hilo: a bowl of rice with a hamburger patty, a fried egg, and brown gravy on top. You know she wrote restaurant reviews for the *The New Yorker* but you don't know her well enough to suggest that her New York palate might be, well, startled. Ruth finds loco moco disgusting, but doesn't say so. Becky decides to try it.

The waitress stands and talks with you and Ruth about her sick auntie for a long time. Becky seems to have worked out that you're regulars at this place, but at the same time it's clear that she's hungry. Get that order slip up on the carousel! Never mind the sick auntie.

The loco moco doesn't seem a success, but Becky gets through it. Much later, she tells you she enjoyed it.

The next morning, Ruth tells you she thinks you made Becky a little uncomfortable with your talking so unreservedly about your intimate feelings on such short acquaintance, and with someone who's much younger. Some of what you told Becky, she says, was appropriate for a therapist to hear, not a young woman who wants to respect you and work collaboratively with you, who's not intending to be your intimate loving friend.

You accept Ruth's criticism, but say that you've been thinking that when Becky writes about you and Jane, she'll be analyzing the guy who's telling her the stories. In other words, you say, not a newspaper profile but something that takes off from deep emotions about the murder and your relationship with Jane, which is hard to separate from the person you were, and have become.

She spends six days talking with you about Jane. You take breaks: hiking in and out of a volcanic crater, taking her to the summit of Mauna Kea and to a field of rare plants. With Ruth, you make the rounds of your favorite Hilo restaurants. You take pictures of each other. But mostly you sit together on a sofa in the living room, and talk.

You don't like admitting your hearing is going, but you don't want to be constantly saying "What?" so you tell her. After that, she's careful to face you and yes, she does raise her voice. Usually.

One night at the house she starts in with family stories and has you and Ruth helpless with laughter. In bed you say, "She could do standup." Ruth laughs and agrees.

# POSITIVES AND NEGATIVES

BEFORE BECKY ARRIVED you found a set of negatives from a portrait session you and Jane did in a house you and another grad student were renting down by MIT. You hadn't looked at them in years, probably because you only remembered a later session in which you shot Jane and Jill in what was then a popular style—high contrast, lots of grain. You had kept a large print of Jane in that style for years, but somehow it hadn't made it through all the moves and to Hilo. The negatives you found were earlier, and pretty much straight. No messing around with exposure and development.

When you put the negatives on the light table tears came to your eyes. *Look at her*, you thought, suddenly remembering that afternoon in a hot room. She'd asked you to photograph her. Floodlights. Your Nikon F with a fast lens. Grey card, light meter.

Jane in a chair, awkward at first, not wanting to *pose*. Saying she didn't know how. You were just getting started as a serious photographer, and hadn't done a portrait session before. Only candids. You told her to play to the camera, play to you, play to the room with its sloping walls and crude bookshelves.

"Be yourself," you said. You hardly knew what you meant by that clichéd command, but in a moment she came alive and energy seemed to flow from her to you through the camera, via her image fleetingly on the ground glass. It didn't matter if she was playing to the camera or to you. Once you learned how she moved her head, her body, you could anticipate even slight movements. You felt as though the two of you were dancing. Afterwards you didn't say anything about how you'd felt, and neither did she. Didn't know how to.

You hadn't sent Becky any of your Jane pictures. When she was in California on her way to Hilo, you made quick scans and emailed them to her, but you weren't ready to write about what you felt in that room.

"Here she is," you wrote. "Beautiful. My heart hurts. These are having a much stronger effect on me than I would ever have predicted. She seems vulnerable."

Becky replied, "I'm speechless. Taxiing on the runway in LAX and I can't stop staring. And if I find them so arresting I can only imagine how they're gripping you."

In one image she's turned slightly to face the camera. One hand's on her hip, the other on a thigh. There's a tautness, as if she's poised to get up and come to the camera. Perhaps to you.

Everything about her says *This is who I am.*

Two years later, Becky chooses that image for her book's cover, although her publisher crops it down to a head shot. You show the image to a friend who has a good eye, and he likes the entire frame. You owe him a favor, so in 2020 when you make a large print for Becky, you make one for him.

When working with the traditional six-frame strips of negatives—as opposed to scrolling through jpgs on a computer screen—there are always frames you never look at closely unless you're running them through an enlarger, and it's been more than 40 years since you had a darkroom.

In Fall 2020 you take the strips from their glassine homes in an Agfa envelope, drop them on the light table again, and find a shot that's so wonderful, so very *Jane*, that you immediately know it's your cover image.

If Becky's image says *This is who I am*, the one you found says *This is how it was.* Cigarette in hand, looking a bit tired, dreamy, no longer high on what's happening, she sits on the same chair against the chimney. Except in this one you see the floodlight, the cluttered side table and instead of the blank chimney wallpaper of the other shots, there's a print of a Japanese god, which now hangs in your son's Brooklyn townhouse.

Ruth, on seeing the image, says "It's sexy. And badass, too."

Just as an anthropologist believes that an outsider sees some parts of a culture more clearly than an insider does—by virtue of not having been immersed in it all his life—you believe that very often a person who has no attachment to, no knowledge or memory of an image will see things the photographer doesn't. He'll be looking for shapes, for patterns in that image made of a person he doesn't know.

You sent your son Ethan, whose visual sense is honed by his professional work as a film and video editor, a cover version with the entire frame inset. Almost immediately he cropped it, manipulated it a bit, and returned to you a perfect cover design.

You hated giving up the floodlights, the books, Jane's pack of Winston cigarettes, the prints on the wall, but Ethan's crop made up for losing...losing what? Context, you supposed, but you willingly gave that up that because the image was so strong.

Years ago you published a story called "Burials," which was, on the surface, about burials both archaeological and non-archaeological. Another theme was the perception of time. In one section, the narrator and his pit partner Suzanne excavate an infant burial.

You went back to that story when you were thinking about those negative strips in their envelopes for so many years, waiting for you and Becky to explore them. For you to situate yourself in that room and immerse yourself in what happened there.

I suppose there are people whose lives can be represented as a single stratigraphic column, but I'm not one of them. Mine seems to move between sites, sometimes occupying several simultaneously. There appear to be unconformities. I haven't found an appropriate dating method for myself yet.

Thinking about process is hard, the answers more elusive and obscure. On a shell midden late in a day in May 1963, I began to understand how past and present can multiply intersect, and how those intersections can either trap us or spit us out.

There's the picture of Suzanne and then there's the burial. The recorded sequence on that day was that I shot Suzanne first, and we uncovered our burial second. The evidence for this is that the two events are recorded next to each other on the orange strip of negatives, and they will stay in that relative position forever, even though the prints made from them have been well plowed.

The only physical evidence of that day left to me are those negatives. The rest is all memory and it isn't fixed in time, but instead exists in that world where the past remains not just alive, but loose, and where the only thing that stays fixed is how we feel when we remember it, and that changes too, but more slowly.

# Pain

You talked to Becky about pain. It was a painful time. The sharp pain of losing someone you loved. Everything accompanying the murder was painful. These pains are simple to describe. After a time they subside. Then they reappear. They never go away.

Sometimes you felt as though you were chopping up your pain so that Becky could understand it. You spoke in bursts. When that happened it was more like taking pieces of pain from a cupboard and showing them, but sometimes you felt as though you were giving her long, flowing sentences about pain as if it were a rolled-up Bijar rug in the attic. That would be the Jane pain.

She was recording, so it didn't matter how you spoke. She didn't have to transcribe verbatim in real time. You remembered what it was like in Nagovisi, where your only recording tools were tape recorders that didn't always work properly. What you wouldn't have given for something like Becky's little Olympus.

You felt pain when your father died, and your mother; their deaths were painful but that's easily understood. When you work with your father's hand tools you think of him and feel his loss; when you use your mother's dishes or open her Chinese chests it's the same.

You tell Becky that you no longer have the rug that the *Globe* trolling had been about, so you can't bring it out and show her the gap along one edge where, years ago, you finally cut out the bloodstain, the last biological link to Jane.

You tell her that for the three decades you were teaching introductory archaeology it was your habit to roll a lab cart filled with artifacts and other useful teaching aids into class every day. You kept the little Solutrean laurel-leaf point and the pottery jaguar face you'd taken from Jane's apartment on it. You never thought of that as keeping Jane near you, but that's what it was. When you picked either of them up to show the students there was a microburst of sadness and pain in your heart. And, often, anger.

Back in your drinking days, you tell her, the pain would turn into rage not just at Jane's death, but at how the police failed to bring the killer to justice. Because you were sure you knew who the murderer was, you would plot ways to make him confess or even to kill him. You wished for every evil thing to befall him. Then he died. Now your anger is at the wrongness of it, its foulness. The killer's death did not right the imbalance.

You get the artifacts from the Japanese *tansu* your mother left you, for Becky to hold; while you're talking about pain and anger she holds the jaguar face, sometimes turning it around, sometimes putting it down on the coffee table and picking it up again, and you hold the point, sometimes enclosing it in your fist.

Each glued-together piece of the face has an accession number on it, which she copies down. You say you think it's Mesoamerican, perhaps Mayan and if so it might be a link to the Mesoamerican archaeologist you think killed her. The Solutrean point, a common French Upper Paleolithic artifact, tells you nothing, although it, too, has an accession number.

By the next day, Becky has learned the face's provenance, and has found photographs of it in an archaeological paper. It's Incan, not Mayan. It's clear that Jane had no right to it and therefore neither do you.

You remember that Jane took in archaeological illustration work, so she was most likely drawing it for some researcher. You decide that, sometime before you die, you'll return it to the Peabody. But not yet.

# EXPOSITION

YOU CAN TELL BECKY's a skilled interviewer; she asks questions but never leads. Quickly you realize she's making you question some of your assumptions. Never by challenge; at most, by gentle prodding: Why do you think that was? Did you ever have a different idea?

When you realize you're too often thinking *Because that's how I've thought about it all these years* you recognize you're probably going to be changing your mind about a few things. And you're looking forward to it.

To answer Becky's questions, to shape your answers, make them responsive and helpful, you're going to have to inhabit Becky's mind in a way you've never had to inhabit an interrogator's mind. It's the difference between having an adversary and having a collaborator.

You need to talk about how Jane existed in the world, not how she existed in your memory. But that's not what you've done over the years as you talked about the murder. It's going to be difficult.

You realize that, for almost half a century, you and Jane and the murder have been a closed system. You've talked about it but—after you left Cambridge—you haven't had to explain yourself to anybody. When you talked about the murder, it was really your story, not Jane's.

But now there's Becky, who has learned more about Jane's life than you ever did, knows a great deal about the murder and the investigation, and is here in Hilo wanting to learn things only you know—such as Jane's nature. What being her friend was like.

You were a piece of the puzzle in 1969, but the puzzle-solvers were dangerous. Sgt. Sennott has again made you a piece of it, and that may be dangerous. Rather than feeling apprehension about what's happening with Becky, you feel an awakening. A pleasure. Everything feels different.

She's made you realize you've been in a bubble all these years, with no new information, no new slants. Your story of Jane's murder ricochets around your head but hasn't delivered anything new for decades.

You can't help wondering how you're going to appear in the book. You're the only one intimately involved in the murder who's talking to Becky. Jane's boyfriend Jim, Jill, a few others—none of them will cooperate. The scientist part of you worries about this. The sample size is too small. You find yourself telling Becky that Jill will remember more about something than you do, or that Jim will, or that Andrea knows everything about how it was in Iran, but there's no help for it.

You assume that Becky will explain why you're the only one. But her readers will wonder whether your story's enough. You mentally shrug. Nothing to be done about it. It's in her hands. You don't doubt that she'll handle it well.

The telling of things to somebody who's listening closely forces you to listen to yourself. Some of what comes out of your mouth doesn't make sense, and you know it immediately, sometimes even before you finish a sentence. You go on to the end anyway. Apologize. Start over.

Like when you describe the time Jane played a Bach organ toccata. You say, "She played it for me at that church on the Cape," but then you realize it wasn't just *you*, because Jill must have been there too, so you say that, and when Becky asks when that was you say, "Wedding rehearsal," and but then you can't remember whether there *had* been a rehearsal, probably not, and you get that out, and finally retreat entirely and wonder whether it was at the Busch-Reisinger Museum, just down Divinity Avenue from the Peabody Museum, and then you retract that because there was no way E. Power Biggs was going to let a student play his organ. Fumble, rephrase, withdraw. Luckily for your self-image, it doesn't happen very often.

From all those years doing fieldwork, interviewing people in a language not your own, you do feel that you're able to see not just where she's going, but sense her alerts and when she's making mental notes about questions she's going to have to rephrase.

And when to say nothing. One afternoon you're talking about your Grand Jury testimony. You'd already told her about the grad student friends with a friend on the Grand Jury who, they told you, said the DA tried to indict you, but the jury wouldn't go along.

You'd given Becky the names and email addresses of those friends, before she came to Hilo, but she'd never told you whether she'd talked to them or whether they'd led her to the Grand Jury leaker. It was only after you'd finished talking about them that she told you she'd interviewed the guy.

You knew better than to ask her what he'd said. Not revealing that you've already talked to somebody is a crucial, and in your own fieldwork you'd done exactly the same thing. To you, this marked her as skilled and, an overused descriptor, *professional*.

Remembering how it was with the police in those interrogation rooms makes you glad you're not in the hands of an adversary. She would be formidable.

In Hilo, even when you don't know where she's headed, you know she's not trying to trip you up. You're not in a precarious spot. You're newly looking within, inspecting what you've said and not said, done and not done, believed and not believed, and you're talking about it freely.

After she's gone, you email her a compliment on her interviewing. She replies, "I was especially aware of my role as an interviewer with you—it's like questioning Terry Gross—you can see the other person clocking your moves," which delighted you. Perhaps you hadn't lost *all* your youthful skills.

You come to understand that even the *right answer*, whatever that means, might not be enough. If all you give her is what you did, what you saw, what happened to you, then what she writes can't have any juice. You've got to give her more to work with.

You're going to have to unmask.

## What You Don't Talk About

You tell Becky there are some things you've never trusted anyone enough to reveal. Not any of your wives. Not any of your men friends. Not even women with whom you were intimate friends. Nobody until Ruth, you say, because you lost her for forty years, and when you're filling in that much time with someone you've fallen back in love with there's little you don't reveal.

One is whether you'd been sexual with Jane.

You knew Becky would ask about that and you knew you'd answer truthfully. The simple answer is "No," but you weren't sure of the best way to explain yourself. You thought about it while walking. You wanted her to know that although desire *was* there, the attraction was more of warmth and intimacy than about carnality.

By the time you needed to talk about attraction, Becky had seen the Jane you knew, which helped.

You were old enough to be Becky's grandfather and you worried that even with the pictures, talking about sweetness and warmth might seem soft-focused, even sentimental. Vaseline on the lens. Dragging down Lightroom's Texture and Clarity sliders.

So how to frame it? Perhaps talk about a summer night after Jane had moved into the apartment next door. You and Jill were a couple, but not married; she was in New Mexico, perhaps for months. It's a short memory clip: Jane sits on your couch, smoking; you're in a chair, drink in hand, facing her. You remember the sexual tension in the room.

"Nothing happened," you tell Becky, "but it was intense."

She makes a note.

"I was afraid she might make a move, and I didn't know what I'd do if she did. And I was sure that if I made a move, she'd respond. So I sat there—we sat there—and I think if we'd locked eyes something would have been launched. Listen to me drop into the passive."

Becky smiles and shifts a bit on the couch. *The self-deprecating subject*, you think, *a lateral move she probably knows well.*

You clear your throat. "But I never imagined what might have happened and masturbated. Does that help you understand?"

Becky nods her head. Writes something in her notebook.

Later that afternoon you could see that Becky was having trouble apprehending those first hours after the murder: the confusion, the fear, the sorrow, the search for an anchor, any anchor.

"I've never told anybody this," you began, hesitating.

Becky nodded her head.

"It was the first night, after we got back from the police station. We had gone to bed. I heard a noise from Jane's apartment. Somebody at her door, or in the hall.

I thought it might be the killer, coming for us. I took her hand and said 'I love you,' which I had never said to her before. And I don't remember ever saying it again."

Telling Becky was like telling Jane.

That night you told Ruth.

# PRIDE

ON ANOTHER DAY you tell Becky something you're not proud of: how you've used the murder.

Every few years, there would be somebody talking about crime, the police, media hysteria, and you've said,

"I've been there."

"I was involved in a murder once."

"I found the body."

"I was sweated by the cops."

"I heard they tried to indict me."

But every time it felt inappropriate—even boastful. Who doesn't know that sometimes the police can be bastards, sometimes the media can be savage, that detectives lie, and people get away with murder? You knew you were calling attention to yourself. Making Jane's murder about you. But you did it anyway.

You tell Becky that cheapened Jane's murder. Made it into nothing but a topic of conversation.

"No," Becky says. "You've been keeping Jane's story alive. You've been spreading it. Making people think about it, talk about it, be affected by it. Jane has become part of their worlds."

You'd never thought about it like that.

You're writing fiction about Jane. You ask Becky if that seems different. It does, she tells you, because your novel will make people think about murder with a capital M, a capital-V victim, capital-P police, and, because you've told her what you intend, capital-G guilt, capital-V vengeance. So it's a different story. The murder's the backdrop.

"To me," she says, "Jane's the centerpiece, Jane and her world. Which included you."

You can't quite put a name to what's bothering you until you remember something Jane's younger brother Boyd wrote to you after you got back in contact. You hadn't talked to him since the funeral.

Boyd was for years a famous Los Angeles radio DJ. Now he's a thoughtful, articulate Episcopal priest, whose emails to you nevertheless do sometimes include the word *fuck*.

He wrote "Someone recently admonished me that harboring guilt is a form of spiritual pride."

The *spiritual* part didn't resonate with you, but the *pride* part did. Maybe that's what the storytelling was really about.

Pride in your rage that the person you thought killed Jane was never charged.

Pride in your hunger for revenge.

Pride in feeling *righteous*.

## The Young You

After the first day, you told Ruth that you trusted Becky, but what you'd interpreted as trust turned out to be something else.

One afternoon in your living room, the two of you sometimes on the couch next to the coffee table littered with notes, letters, a pair of MacBooks, sometimes in the dining room with its stacks of slide boxes, negative folders, movie film, the light table and loupes, then returning to talk about what you'd looked at, it seemed to you that Becky was as comfortable in those surroundings as you were, and there was nothing you were doing that either you or she would do differently.

When you asked yourself why, the answer came quickly.

It was because Becky, so alive, filled with curiosity and ability, was doing what you had longed to do at her age, which was to tell untold stories, to write what hadn't been written, to bring the past to life. To make art.

Which made her the young you.

Except when you were young you'd closed the door on all that, and she hadn't.

You could see that Becky was trying to live Jane's life, which meant that Jane might return to life in her. At your age you would never live Becky's life. But her success might open the world again for you, and this time you would not close the door. Entry would be a gift from Jane.

# Drum Noise Is Just Drum Noise

WHEN YOU TAKE BECKY BACK to the airport you ask one of the workers to take a picture of the three of you: Becky, you, Ruth, arms around each other. Smiling. It's night and the background is dark. The three of you could have been anywhere, doing anything. There's nothing to suggest the bond that's developed between you and Becky in the last six days, a bond that resists categorization. *Common purpose* comes close.

Some time after Becky leaves, you get a phone call from Boyd. Sgt. Sennott has interviewed him and taken his DNA, because Massachusetts has no bits of Jane left.

Boyd says that damping down the talking about this case would be good. *Don't help Becky and Todd beat the drum,* your scrawled note of the conversation reads, *drum noise is just drum noise. Nothing the DA could release would help the investigation.*

You make noises of agreement because Boyd's talking about *solving* the case. He's got a point. Releasing information about the case will advance Becky but probably won't help solve it.

Still, you're certain that the noise Todd, Becky, Michael and Alyssa made is what got the authorities moving, got Sgt. Sennott on an airplace to California and—soon—to Hilo. So, in your view, it had helped the investigation. Clearly, though, Boyd's talking about the present.

All those people in Massachusetts, even Sgt. Sennott on the phone, complain about "people making money off this," as if that were the only issue. Why should we release information just so somebody can write a book and make money? You don't doubt that there's some of that in Jill's and Andrea's refusal to help, too.

But really. Is Becky's sole interest making money? You know that's not the case. And why is she the only one people complain about? The *Globe* article said you were writing a novel about it, so why aren't people getting after you? Maybe *The New Yorker* stands for everything they hate, but an old guy in Hawai'i doesn't?

Sitting in your workroom looking at your screen, which is showing what you hope's going to become a novel, you know your motives are mixed. You want to build on Jane's story in fiction, where you won't have to worry about what really happened, and you think of that as your tribute to her, yes, but you're trying to advance your own writing career, to emerge from the provincial old guy author gloom, into some exposure, perhaps some praise, perhaps some important contacts.

So who's clean here?

## CAUSING PAIN

BACK IN APRIL you wondered whether *you* might suffer because Becky, Todd and the others were poking the District Attorney bear. At that point you didn't think of *yourself* as a bear-poker or a log in the flood or a spider, much less a snake or a tsunami, a danger to others, but that was because you hadn't bothered thinking about what might happen when you tried to help Becky by pushing Andrea to reveal Jane's old boyfriend's contact information, and by giving Sgt. Sennott her email so he could ask her the same thing. That injected Andrea into this mess, and she didn't like it. You knew that both Sgt. Sennott and Becky wanted to talk to Jill and you told them how to contact her, knowing already that she didn't want to talk.

In June, you email Becky about your fear, "actual fear, not different from what I felt back then." You worry that there might be some way that the investigation might twist and snare you.

She replies that she's been wondering your emotional experience, and the pain that "unearthing this has caused." Andrea's son—whom you held at his bris— asked her to "consider the suffering reopening old wounds causes," and that she finds it hard to justify that it's worth it. She writes that she sees "the waves of worry it's causing you and it's hard. I know deep down it's important to shed light on Jane's story, and that this is far from just an exercise in creating something commercial, but I'm extremely aware of the hurt I'm causing."

You find yourself worrying more about Becky than about yourself. Yes, there's that worry about being snared, but when you inspect that dispassionately you see that the risk is very, very small because it requires that unknown people in Massachusetts have decided to frame you and are going to tell lies or manipulate the lab work. And you know that's extremely unlikely. The Massachusetts lab worker caught falsifying drug tests wasn't working homicide.

Any hurt is coming from within you. And what difference does that make, really? It's not going to affect anything you do, any work or writing you're going to do, except perhaps to wake you in the night.

It's not the same for Becky, who has a goal and intends to—needs to—reach it. You tell her not to worry about your feelings, that you see her as an ally. Then you write, "As for the others and their non-cooperation, I have harsh feelings for them, in today's speech, 'don't be such a snowflake.' Only want to see things sorted out if there's no cost to you? Well, fuck you then."

Their unwillingness seems disrespectful. Isn't Jane worth some pain, now as in the past? It's not as though the others, who presumably loved her as you did, were sticking up for *her*. They aren't assisting the investigation, shibai or not. They aren't allowing Becky to tell their sides of the story, their pieces of the truth. They're only thinking about themselves, which in your mind is selfish.

It's as though they can't distinguish between "look at me!" and "look at this!"

Jill lost the urge to follow new leads long before you did. More than twenty years ago you told her that the crime writer Susan Kelly had called to talk about the cigarette butt (found in Jane's ashtray, but not the brand she smoked) and whether you thought DNA could be lifted from it. "Oh, why did you bother?" Jill said, and you replied, "I'm always going to bother."

You write Becky, "I was talking to Ruth in the kitchen. She said, with regard to any pain you'd cause or wounds you'd open—'Becky's making art and that's what happens.'"

# On the Road

AFTER BECKY LEFT and you resumed your eight and nine hour walks, you began questioning yourself. Privately, you imagined that Becky's success might advance you. That coattails thing. That you might—you wince when you think about it, because it's such an obvious thing—get yourself at least to the periphery of the Big Time. It does seem venal, even though your conscience is clear: when you said that you'd help her any way you could, you meant it absolutely, and you've delivered, with pleasure. If nothing happens that advances you, well, you have that intensely satisfying time with her, which gave you an internal boost if nothing else. Right? It's something to think about while walking.

One day in late fall, after you and Ruth had been in Brooklyn to see your grandchildren and had spent time with Becky, you were walking up the Saddle Road. You'd planned to do 14 or 15 miles; it was an out-and-back so you could turn back any time you wanted to. About seven miles out, you felt strong and decided to go for something in the 20 mile range. Water would be an issue, but you remembered that on one of your very long walks you hadn't used all of your ten-mile cache; when you'd picked up after yourself the next day you'd left a quart of Gatorade hidden in a tall clump of grass. If it was still there, you'd be fine. If not, you'd have to make it to the public water tap about six miles down from where you'd turn, which would be tough but not dangerous. You decided to go for it.

Up there on the Saddle you were, not surprisingly, thinking about your novel and about Becky's work. You thought about how Becky was doing a kind of ethnography. It wouldn't be much of a book if she focused only on Jane and her path. You knew she wouldn't—she hadn't come to see you only to talk about the murder itself. She had to understand the social system, the culture of the Anthropology Department, the Museum, the students. How could Jane be understood except in context?

On one of those days she'd asked you to talk about what Jane was like, and you hadn't done a very good job answering. You could talk about her manner, but that involved broad brushstrokes. How did she think? You couldn't answer a question like that. What were her politics? You had no idea, beyond that they were leftish. You knew the kind of music she liked, but you can't remember her ever talking about it beyond her suggesting, if she was over, what album she'd like you to play.

Boyd had turned over Jane's letters, so Becky would be able to get into Jane's head that way. They would give an intimate window into her psyche. You didn't learn about this until after Becky had left, or you'd have told her how, when you'd been going through your old letters, you'd been amused (and sometimes saddened) by the young man you saw in them. You'd given Becky many of those letters, but you didn't know how she'd use them. She wasn't writing a book about you, for all that you knew you'd appear in it.

In July, before Sgt. Sennott arrived, you wrote Becky about not only your worries, but about what you thought had happened to you since you began working with her:

My mental image of what's been happening is that trees have fallen and what looked like impenetrable forest that I didn't even recognize, much less think about entering, is now semi-open country with interesting new trails running through it.

But that didn't get you into Jane's head. It only helped you see the landscape she inhabited.

You thought about how you were interested in the *consequences* of the murder. Your novel was only indirectly about Jane—about Kate, the fictional Jane. But the only voice Kate had was as reported by Elliot. The reader was never in her head. It was about what happened after she was killed, how it affected people, about retribution and revenge and guilt. It's not as though this came to you as a flash of insight. You knew what you were writing. What came to you on the road was a clarification, a heightening of the sense you already had.

You were aware of the danger of making Kate little more than a plot device so that the real business of the novel could proceed. You'd done that once before, in *News of Elsewhere*, when you needed a village girl to have an affair with one of your characters and then die after her attempt to abort herself of his child. Then things would get very messy for everybody, especially Elliot, because he ended up, with the local medical orderly, trying and failing to save her, and was the only person who both knew about the affair and why she'd died. She told him—it only required two words—as she was dying. And he blamed himself for her death because he had been told about the procedure from some older women, and told her about it, never thinking she'd have a reason to use it. She prepared the potion incorrectly.

So you wrote a draft of that section. When you read it to yourself you realized that you'd created a character for no other purpose than to have sex with somebody and die.

You left your room, went upstairs to Ruth's, told her what the problem was, and said "it's chickenshit and I can't do it." Then you went back down and began developing that character, who became one of your favorites. You loved her—Lakabula, a teenage Nagovisi girl. When you wrote her death, tears came to your eyes.

*Well,* you said to yourself, *am I doing the same thing with Kate?*

The simple answer was yes. But at that point what you were planning for Elliot and Kate was a brief affair that began after he returned and ended, two weeks later, with her death. So although the novel would be richer if she had a voice, it wasn't essential.

The swirling worlds of fiction and nonfiction was one you and Becky hoped to inhabit together: she would produce the one, you, the other. A pairing.

On the road, tiring, a little thirsty, heart rate up but steady, you knew you were indulging yourself in a dream. That wasn't a bad way to pass the time on a twenty-miler, but you knew that's all it was. Becky had an agent and a New York publisher. You didn't even have a complete draft of your novel, or an agent, much less a publisher.

*Ah, stop worrying about it,* you thought, feeling around in the tall grass for the bottle of Gatorade and finding it, wiping it on your singlet and drinking, *it's gonna play out how it plays out.*

You thought about tacking on another three miles up, three back, giving yourself a marathon, but decided not to. It was getting hot, and there'd be a headwind. You crossed the highway, turned, and headed down the mountain.

# Mauna Kea

You know a great deal about Mauna Kea, the nearly 14,000' dormant volcano across the Saddle from Mauna Loa, also nearly 14,000', but active. You like to say to people that you've been knocking around on it for more than sixty years. You know the higher slopes and the lower ones. You were on it as a boy and, now that you're back on the Big Island, not many weeks go by but what you and Ruth are somewhere on it in your Toyota 4Runner, a 4WD vehicle that can tackle any of its roads and tracks.

Mauna Kea has been contested territory for the last fifteen years or so, and the site of large, organized protests against the observatories at its summit, and a planned new one. The reasons are complex, the solutions difficult, perhaps even out of reach. This isn't the place to untangle it all, or even lay it out.

In 2016 you were invited to join an organization—EnVision Maunakea—that hoped to decrease tensions by gathering people to talk about Mauna Kea: what it meant to them, how they used it, how they saw its future. One intent was to tap what was believed to be a large population of people who knew and cared about the entire mountain—not just the summit and the observatories, which are the contested spaces. They were cultural practitioners, ranchers, business people, scientists, hunters, artists, elders, students, environmentalists, and activists. There was no litmus test but, as it happened, the protesters who were invited refused to participate.

The format was small, closed meetings at which the guests would talk and a group that included you would listen—the Listening Group, or in Hawaiian, the Hui Hoʻolohe. You were attracted to the group—and they to you—because listening to people talk was what you'd spent years doing as an anthropologist, and you were good at it, if a bit out of practice. The meetings—called Listening Sessions—were safe spaces where no one interrupted anyone else, no one argued, and everyone was treated with the respect due them. As a Listener, you occasionally asked a question but spent most of your time taking in what was being said.

When Becky came to Hilo, you were already at work, and excited about it. The sessions were going well and you were pleased by how easily you fell back into your field working frame of mind. You were excited by the passions you saw, and the depth of knowledge the guests brought to the sessions. You began to believe that you could *do some good*, a feeling you hadn't had for many years. You began to see yourself as an active member of the community rather than, as had always been your preference, someone off to the side—if not in the shadows then at the dimly-lit margins. But here, even as a passive Listener, you were using your skills and training. It was satisfying.

When Becky came you must have told her about it, but you wouldn't have gone into detail. Even so, you did sometimes think of Becky as your own Listener, in front of whom you were thrust, or thrust yourself, to center stage.

There were no meetings during the week she was in Hilo, but they happened at intervals all through 2017. That year was a difficult one for you. For periods, you lost courage and were depressed about Jane, about your novel. But the prospect of a Listening Session always lifted your spirits, because although you never knew what would happen, you knew it would be interesting.

After the sessions ended late that year, it was time to write a report. At first, there was talk of a traditional report in the style everybody knew. Executive summary, bullet points, list of recommendations, references. You didn't want to take a role in writing it, at least partly because your novel was going poorly, the excitement of being part of Becky's project had died down, and you weren't quite feeling yourself, although you didn't know why.

You agreed to help distill the hours of talk so that a report could be written. You didn't want to impose yours or anyone else's categories on the material, to force it into some pre-defined shape. Instead, you let the categories emerge from it.

Then, without thinking it would be taken seriously, you suggested writing a different kind of report, one that you envisioned as ethnography—a report written in the voices of the people who had spoken, not of the report-writers. It seemed to you that was the best way to show both those in power and those who opposed them that there were, on the Big Island, thoughtful voices that were not being heard. Your group called them the "soft voices."

The group agreed. And so, with input from three other Listeners, you wrote that report, illustrated it with your photographs, and, because you'd by then been designing books for years, set it up for printing. It was, you thought, a handsome publication. Because it was the report of the Hui Hoʻolohe as a group, it went out over the Hui's name, not yours, which was, as is said in Hawaiʻi, *pono* (righteous, proper).

People were expecting the typical boring report you hadn't wanted to make, so your work surprised them. They were also expecting a set of recommendations, and the Hui was dead-set against making any of its own.

At first, people didn't know what to make of it—what *was* this thing?—but it began to gain traction, and not just for itself, but because the entire structure—the listening groups, the different style of report—showed how barriers could be broken down and previously-unheard voices be heard. And because people found it easy to read, they *did* read it, and the soft voices were heard.

Thousands of copies were printed and distributed. You were proud of what the group had done, and of what you'd done. The Governor asked some of you to come over to Honolulu and talk to him, and you did. Twice.

You sent Becky a copy. You sent your other writing friends copies, too.

# WALKING

In your sixties, when you weren't running anything more than 20 miles, you started taking long walks. In Hilo during the winter of 2010 you'd gotten your mileage up a bit. You had the idea to walk from your house up the Saddle Road to the place on Mauna Kea where you'd buried your parents' ashes. You'd have to climb more than 9,000'. Most of the walk would be on the Saddle Road, which climbed out of Hilo into a saddle between Mauna Loa and Mauna Kea.

You hadn't been on foot on the Saddle Road since 1978, when, visiting from Buffalo, you joined a pick-up team of four other 30-something runners and took second overall in a 100k relay race from Hilo to Waimea. You weren't certain how far this walk it would be—about 30, you thought. It turned out to be just over 32 miles, and it took you about nine hours. And you loved it.

When you returned to the 19th century farmhouse in Colden, New York that you and Ruth lived in, you were still thinking about that 32 miler. You remembered that back in the seventies, your younger running friends sometimes talked about "running your age"—a mile for every year. They were in their twenties, so it was doable.

You'd biked your age a few times, but that was easy.

True, there was that 50 miler, in which you'd passed 37 miles, your age then, well before the end. But in your mind, that didn't count.

You realized you could probably walk your age in *kilometers*. Not miles—that was beyond you by then.

Just getting to the end wouldn't do it for you. You wanted to do it around your birthday, a few weeks either way, and to make it a form of walking meditation. By then you'd tried Buddhist walking mediation, although you didn't consider yourself a practitioner, particularly because you hadn't become very good at being *in the moment*. Your monkey mind raced around, untamed. So this would be a kind of contemplation, rather than meditation. And much longer: during each kilometer you would reflect on who you were and what you were doing at that age.

You trained. You knocked off a couple of twenties, then a thirty, and then in June, your birth month, you went 67k, 41.6 miles, on the Colden roads.

Some kilometers were more meaningful than others. When your GPS watch showed 21k you thought, *First date with Ruth.* Back in 1964, you had only three months together—250 meters. You looked down the road and were startled to realize how quickly you and she would go your separate ways. After that you'd have to walk almost a marathon before, at 61k, you'd see her again.

That year and every year after that you texted her from 21k, then 21.25k and again at 61k.

You remember the first time you got to 25k and thought about being 25. There was a lot to contemplate. You were newly married to Jill. That summer, you'd left her in Cambridge and gone to do research on Malaita, in the Solomon Islands, and then had made your way to Bougainville and asked the Nagovisi if you and she could live with them, and they'd agreed. You promised to return early in 1969.

You thought about Jane, who was killed midway through that year. You thought about the turmoil. You wondered, as you always did, what the DA thought he had on you. You thought about arriving in Nagovisi to take up residence and start doing research.

When you and Ruth moved to Hilo, the contemplation walks became much more difficult. The only practical route was up the Saddle Road. The first 43k (about 27 miles) were almost entirely uphill, gaining nearly 7,000' from your house. At about 7,500' elevation it leveled out, and then finally, after a nasty but short hill at 61k, the rest was a welcome steady downhill.

Every year you wore the same shirt, a lime-green long sleeved one from the Hilo to Volcano 50k, in which you'd done well, but not well enough to get an award. That one had only climbed 4,000'.

On most of the Saddle Road the shoulders were wide, so you didn't have to pay close attention to the traffic. You felt very much alone, even though, technically, you weren't. Up there you never saw another walker or runner. Just you, the road, the wind, the altitude. Occasionally a wild pig. Once some endangered nene geese flew low over you. Helicopters from the Army training base, tourist helicopters. You ignored them. An occasional car stopped by the side of the road, so that people could run into the bushes or behind lava outcroppings to piss. One year, on the other side of the road, an older woman in a chair, singing.

A few cyclists. On your 76k walk one crossed over to chat. He and some friends were heading for the summit of Mauna Kea for the first time. You warned him about the long stretch of rock and gravel road before the pavement near the summit. Then, because you didn't think he was taking the altitude seriously enough, and was talking about how much fun it would be to rocket down, you said—choosing your words carefully—"Watch it coming down. You're going to be fucked up from the altitude." He looked at you, perhaps not expecting an old guy to say "fucked up." So you said it again: "The altitude fucks with your thinking. You can get stupid up there."

You knew this because of all the times you'd hiked to the summit, exhausted when you got there, and had been aware you were fucked up. As you hiked back down, your head would clear. You'd been hiking to Mauna Kea's summit since you were fourteen, long before there was a road beyond the 9,300' level.

You saw plenty of cars and 18-wheelers. The big rig drivers often waved; the car drivers, almost never. Sometimes you wondered what the people in cars thought. *What the hell is that guy doing?* One year you posted your walk on Facebook and a friend commented that he'd seen you on his way to Kona to shop at Costco and he'd seen you on the way back, too.

You loved walking up the Saddle, at least partly because of the challenge. The birthday walks took a long time, so you started from the house in the dark, usually with a headlamp, which you stashed in the bushes when you no longer needed it. Before sunrise, the wind blows downslope from the mountains, and after the day gets going, it blows upslope from the shore. For the first two hours you were in the dark, it was cold, and there was a headwind. Then the wind always shifted, and you got a warm tailwind.

After the highest point, you were going down the other side of the island, which meant your tailwind was replaced by a headwind, which could be brutal because by then you were tiring. One year you hit heavy fog and rain on the down side and that was the only time you worried about your safety on a 60 mph 3-lane road.

You'd learned where the hills were steep and not so steep. You felt on intimate terms with the shoulder and its paving. You knew where it had crumbled, where were were stones. You knew the blind curves where you had to watch for careless drivers. The first 20 miles or so were mainly forested, but then you hit lava fields, then grasslands. Not a bit of shade, because the sun was never low enough for any fringing trees to cast shadows. After 10k, no human settlements. No water before a park at 52k.

On the climb, you were careful to keep your heart rate between 130 and 140 except on some steep hills, where you let it get to 150 or a little more. You never worried about your HR on the short stuff, but when you knew you'd be climbing steadily for 7 hours, you were careful.

You had your supply caches: about 10 miles, about 20 miles, about 30 miles, and after that you were on your own. You'd go up the day before and set them up: Gatorade, PowerBars, Gu gels, Vaseline, and ibuprofen. One year, rats got into your 10 mile cache and ate the PowerBars but left the Gu, so you were all right. Another year when you went to open the 20 mile paper bag there was a large spider in it. You don't like spiders but you needed your supplies, so you reached in slowly and the spider, perhaps sluggish from the cold, didn't attack.

At the top of a long really steep hill, a nasty 2 mile stretch that began just before 25k, there was a roadside memorial for a guy who'd lost control of his car, crashed, and died: flowers, sometimes food, sometimes notes—the standard memorial stuff. But there was also an orange traffic cone, and every time you wondered why. So his friends wouldn't miss it when they went to leave flowers? You usually stopped there for a Gu.

Each year, a kilometer—.6 mile—longer.

When Becky came to Hilo you were preparing for 74k (46 miles) which is why, on the first day you were to start talking about Jane, you got up early and ripped off 28 miles before meeting her. It went well and you weren't cramping, and only normally sore by the time you, Becky, and Ruth went down to Ken's House of Pancakes for dinner.

And the day after she left, you went 52k up the Saddle, finishing at the old Fish and Game camp—now a state park—where you'd worked the summer after the tsunami. Ruth said you looked tired, and you were, but you shrugged it off because you felt ready.

Two weeks later you nailed the 74k. At 25.5k—January 1969—you took a picture of your watch, typed "thinking of Jane," and sent it to Becky. Later that day, she texted that the image was, "so touching."

Sgt. Sennott arrived a month later.

## The Hawai'i Police Department

July, 2017. As Sgt. Sennott's visit nears, you get nervous. A visiting friend is writing a non-fiction book about a murder, so you tell him the story over dinner. You tell him what leaked out of the Grand Jury, that the DA had pushed for an indictment of you but couldn't get it. That you've never learned what they thought they had on you. He explodes. Says you're "fucking insane" if you don't get a lawyer. Ruth agrees.

Hilo has a couple of criminal defense lawyers, but they don't return your calls. The voice mails you leave seem pretty weird, even to you. You suspect they're not interested in working on something so old, or perhaps it doesn't strike them as something requiring legal help. One of them is a major player in right-wing local politics. Even though you're feeling exposed, you tell yourself you wouldn't want a right-winger giving you advice anyway.

You're going into it bare naked. But can you protect yourself a little?

The Cambridge dicks showed up and did any damn thing they pleased. Maybe you can show Sgt. Sennott that *he* can't. In Massachusetts, you were an outsider. Here, *he's* the outsider.

He suggested meeting at the police station. You like that idea, because you know you can get the local cops to back you up. Hilo looks after its own.

At the station you talk through the speaker to the young officer behind the thick glass. As you're explaining the situation, you expect him to roll his eyes at the "48 years ago" part and tell you not to worry about it.

But he doesn't.

He comes out, sits you down at a table and asks for your ID. You give him your Hawai'i driver license, which tells him where you live, but not that you were born and raised in Hilo, making you *kama'aina*, a child of the land. You recognize the name on his tag and are sure you went to high school with his father. No, grandfather.

Instead of using that, you drop into your local accent, and when he's confirming your address you say, "Yes, Lower Pi'ihonua," the correct name of your neighborhood. Newcomers may know Pi'ihonua but Upper and Lower is locals only.

He nods his head. Done.

You tell him that Sgt. Sennott never sent a state-dot-ma-dot-us email or letter on letterhead, so maybe he's not what he seems. In truth you don't doubt him, but that's not the point. You're counting on the officer to translate: *Can we make sure he knows he's on our turf, not his?*

The cop can't understand why Sgt. Sennott is coming in person, because the Police Department gets DNA requests all the time; they do the swabbing and ship the kits back.

"He talked about chain of custody," you say, and the officer shakes his head. "Guy probably wants a vacation," and both of you laugh.

"But it's not right," he says. "He should have ID'd himself better. Get his badge number and we'll check him out."

He goes inside and returns carrying a police report form, which he's filled out for you. "Have this Massachusetts guy call the CIS here, and they'll check him out for you."

You thank him and pocket the form. He's going off duty so you walk out together. You're tempted to ask about his grandfather, but resist. You've gotten exactly what you wanted.

You drive home to Lower Pi'ihonua, where you text Sgt. Sennott, asking him call the Hilo station CIS and give them his badge number, so they can check it with the Massachusetts State Police.

You have to go to a Listening Session on the other side of the island; on the way, Sgt. Sennott texts you three times and leaves a voice mail saying that he's finally found the right person to talk to, all's well, and that he'll see you tomorrow.

You don't respond because you're enjoying your *Don't fuck with us* feeling.

## The Interview Room

YOU'VE BEEN THINKING about how the whole interview
thing could go wrong. You're thinking about the Grand
Jury. Back you go to the first few minutes after the phone
call. It's the Taipan snake thing. Maybe Sgt. Sennott,
somewhere out there, is more dangerous than you know.

Years ago, when you lived in Buffalo, you were
standing in a 7-11, talking to a prosecuting attorney
who lived in the neighborhood about a case in the news
that turned on a confession. So you told her about the
Cambridge cops.

"You had a lawyer?"

"No."

"What? What?"

"I hadn't done anything wrong."

"That was...stupid. You could be in jail, you don't
know the kinds of shit they can do to you, and you had
no protection."

"I know."

"Don't do it again."

"I won't."

But you have.

In the days before the interview, texts and emails fly between you and Becky.

> He said once again that neither he nor the police have been able to find Jim. I said, "Well, Toronto someplace is all I know."
>
> But really, WTF? You found him...but the Mass State Police and the Mounties can't? Somebody's not working very hard here.
>
> It gets better. He said, "You know, with that woman writing the book, and those two guys poking around and making trouble...we don't want stuff getting out...if we get a reason not to, we don't have to...." That's more a paraphrase than a quote, but whoa. If that's not a shibai admission I don't know what might be. Active investigation! I made no comment.
>
> He said he'd like to "talk about 1969," which I took to mean the obvious. I don't see any reason not to talk in general terms, or even sometimes in detail. I was telling Ruth about this, just now, and she reminded me that it would be awfully nice if the case did break open in some way. And so do I hope (and you) thus I won't stonewall. I won't underestimate him.

On the morning of the interview you text Becky. You tell her how you plan to behave, how you plan to confront him about shibai, what you'll do if you think he's bullshitting you. And, of course, what you'll wear.

> ...long pants? Nah, that means I think it's formal. So, shorts. But t-shirt? Nah, too casual. So it's

shorts + nice aloha shirt. I may be over thinking this whole damn thing. I don't think so, but certainly it's possible. I will try to be supple.

At the Police Station you go to what you thought was the main entrance—the same place you'd gone to get the police on your side—only to be told it was the lockup, not the front desk. An officer walks you over to a side door and shows you into the criminal investigation section. You feel rather stupid. Not a good place to be in when facing an interview you're nervous about.

But everybody's pleasant. You shake hands with Sgt. Sennott and with Lt. Chong, a Hilo detective, who shows the two of you to an interview room and tells you to take as long as you need.

He closes the door on his way out, and there you are again, in a police interview room with a detective. The years fall away. It's 1969 in the Cambridge PD down in Central Square.

You recover quickly. You sit down at the table. He takes out a Macbook Air, which impresses you. You'd have guessed he'd have a government-issue Dell or HP. It changes the way you think of him, which you realize is silly but you go with it anyway.

He gives you a Massachusetts State Police shoulder patch, which seems strange. You think, *Wait…if the MSP's going to try to nail me here, why would they give me a patch? So I know who's after me? Weird.* But you take it anyway, and you still have it. Maybe someday you'll frame it.

You take your field recorder out of your messenger bag, put it on the table and tell him you're going to record the interview. You don't ask; you declare. He says fine, no problem, and will you give him a copy before you leave the room? "Yes," you say, "of course." You didn't bring any cables but you know the Air has an SD slot, so you can eject the card from your recorder and he can copy it.

He asks you to call him Peter. He talks about a MSP detective, now dead, named Lt. Joyce, with whom you'd had a good relationship and had stayed in contact with for years. "I'd like to be your Lt. Joyce," he says. You think it's a bit early for that, but it's a good sign.

After the DNA swabbing you'd agreed unconditionally to do, you call him on the shibai. You weren't going to do an interview without bringing it up, because the worry, the dread, the defensive moves—none of them mean shit if getting your DNA is shibai. Also, not calling him on it would make you a feel a coward.

"In Hawaii we have a word that we use, 'shibai,' and it's a Japanese word, meaning basically smokescreen," you say. "I'm having a hard time believing that this investigation is really active again. I don't think it's a coincidence that you called me right after the *Globe* article went up."

He says, "It's never been closed, it has been investigated."

You say, "Is this just a show that's being put on?"

"We care."

"I kinda need to be convinced that Massachusetts is really working on this."

"There is stuff."

Well. You did what you promised yourself you would. After "There is stuff" you knew you wouldn't get anything more, so you let it go.

It was on. And it was good.

You spent a couple of hours with him, talking about everything he wanted to talk about, and some things you wanted to talk about. You drew diagrams and initialed them. You responded to questions even when you suspected he was misleading you. He responded to some of your questions with what seemed misleading answers.

He flashed a picture of Jane's body just long enough for you to see what it was, but before he could say anything you said, "I don't need to see more pictures of Jane's body," and it went upside down onto the pile.

He seemed not to know about some objects in Jane's bedroom, like the headstone everyone knew about. It had even been in the papers. He couldn't explain why the crime scene photographer seemed to have missed panning around the room, which told you he knew all about it, where it had been, but wanted you to talk before he showed you.

And then he didn't. And you didn't press him.

You let all these things go because you knew you were in a post-truth world. You didn't expect Peter to tell the truth, so it didn't bother you when you thought he wasn't. You did expect him to act like a detective, to lie when it suited him, to pretend he knew things he didn't, or not to know things he did. You expected him to trick you, or try to trap you. Neither of you was under oath, so he could say anything that suited his purposes. And so could you.

Your defense was your absolute right to say "fuck this," shut off your recorder and walk out.

And if it was shibai then nothing that happened in the room mattered anyway.

About an hour in, you realized you liked him. You liked his manner. You liked the way he was treating you. You no longer cared whether he was tricking you or not. You began to enjoy talking about the case, sometimes talking about yourself, with him. Sometimes it felt as though you were joining forces. It didn't take much longer before you stopped thinking he or the DA or the Massachusetts State Police were out to get you, perhaps to frame you. You weren't sure about the shibai, but you were increasingly sure you had nothing to fear.

You asked him about the cigarette butt Susan Kelly had asked you about. He said a cigarette butt didn't figure into anything he was working on, and in the recording you're heard saying "Shit! I had a lot of hope for that cigarette butt, I'll tell you."

## TELL ME EVERY BAD THING

YOU'D SENT PETER COPIES of your correspondence with
Lt. Joyce. In one exchange, ten years after the murder,
you and Lt. Joyce were discussing information that had
emerged about Lee Parsons, an archaeologist on the
Peabody Museum staff, whom you had long believed was
the killer. Lt. Joyce wrote, "I am still of the opinion that
he could have been involved." By that time you no longer
thought Lt. Joyce suspected you, but there *was* the Grand
Jury thing. So you were cooperative, but wary.

Because Lt. Joyce's own files were said to have been lost,
you figured you'd have to explain why you thought Lee had
killed Jane, although Peter probably knew the story.

It went back to a cop who forced a wrenching turn in
your vision of Jane.

One day that January, a detective sitting in your living
room said, "Tell me about Jane," so you and Jill started
in about how wonderful she was. He stopped you. "She
wasn't killed because she was wonderful. She was killed
because she made somebody angry enough to kill her. So
tell me every bad thing you know about her."

You were startled. That she might have been murdered
because of something *she'd* done had never occurred to you.

122

That seemed wrong. You'd been thinking of the murder as a one-way street. Simple causation: murderer, weapon, victim. The killer wanted to kill her, so he did.

You and Jill fumbled for responses. Nothing came quickly. The detectives knew she'd borrowed money from you and other students to go to another state for an abortion. You couldn't think how that might have angered anybody. She could be mean and sarcastic, but how could a cutting remark lead someone to kill her?

But then you widened your thinking. You thought about how she'd been saying she wasn't ready for the comprehensive exam. It was the first year that written comps had replaced the oral exams you'd sat for, which meant nobody knew what they would be like, and that you'd had no advice to give her. Back in the days of orals everybody fussed about not being ready, so you didn't take Jane seriously when she did.

What if she really wasn't ready? What if she thought she'd do poorly? Or even fail? Because she was so highly visible, it would be a disaster. A humiliation. From there it was a short step to wondering whether, in desperation, she might have tried to put pressure on somebody to reveal questions, or to influence the grading. To have done that kind of *bad thing*.

But who? And how?

You, Jill, and Jane had spent a late and drunken night with Lee at his Cambridge apartment. When he lit a cylinder of what he said was centuries-old Mayan incense, and seemed far more wasted than alcohol alone should have made him, you and Jill got nervous. The incense, on a metal platter, scorched the carpet. You didn't like the vibe. You asked Jane if she wanted to leave with you, but she didn't. So you went home without her.

The next day, by chance, you were in the hall as Jane was climbing the stairs. She looked not only hungover but frightened, and wouldn't talk about what happened. And when Lee came looking for her a few days later, Jane, over in your apartment, ran and hid in your bedroom...what had *that* been about? She never said.

Had something happened between them that was so career-endingly bad for him that she thought to trade it for information, for help? You didn't want to call it by its name: *blackmail.*

That's what you told the detective. That's what you thought she might have done that made somebody angry enough to kill her. Saying it hurt terribly, but you did it in service of nailing the killer. You could live with what you did if it were true. You never saw Jane as a saint; none of you were.

In those days people didn't say "blame the victim" in the way we do now, but you were aware that that's what you were doing. Perhaps she brought it on herself. No, wait. She brought *murder* on herself? But it was the only thing you could think of to tell the detective. And even years later, when you were telling Becky about it, you were uncomfortable suggesting it.

You never learned how the detectives turned that into a theory of the crime, if they did, but you know how you did.

It went like this: Lee, having rethought his part of the deal—which would also have been career-ending if revealed—and being angry about it, turns up at Jane's apartment, perhaps to renege or insist on a guarantee of silence and back it up with a threat. He was probably drunk, or high, or both. They argue. He loses it, strikes her in the forehead with the stone tool that was in her turtle tank, she goes down, and he realizes this is not just a career-ending situation but a criminal one. Assault, grievous bodily harm. And there's no way out.

So he kills her.

That became your theory of the murder, less because you believed it made sense than because it emerged from thinking about *every bad thing*.

## Killed by Lightning on a Mayan Pyramid

Peter wants to talk more about Lee. He doesn't seem to know much about him, which you think may mean he doesn't want to lead you. Even so, this seems odd to you because after the murder, Lee was talked about as a suspect among the students. And by Lt. Joyce, though indirectly.

"There's a strange tale here," you tell Peter.

One night in the late seventies, Gene Ogan, an old friend from grad school, called from Minnesota to say that Dennis Puleston, an archaeologist in his department, had told him that Lee had said, while drunk, "I killed someone."

When Ogan called, Puleston was in Guatemala, so Ogan couldn't press him for more details. You remember his saying that he'd talk to Puleston after he got back. After all these years, you're not clear whether Lee allegedly told Puleston himself, or whether he told someone else, who in turn told Puleston. The only thing you're sure of is that Puleston told Ogan what Lee had said.

Said drunkenly or not, this seemed powerful evidence to you. You wrote Lt. Joyce and told him about it, and said that Ogan had said the situation was tricky. Departmental politics, you remember, but that's all. Still, you hoped for the best.

While Ogan was waiting, Puleston climbed to the top of a Mayan pyramid, where he was struck by lightning and killed.

You want to say "You can't make this shit up," but that seems disrespectful, so you don't. Peter shakes his head, and presses for more details, but you don't have any.

You never learned whether Lt. Joyce talked to Puleston or to Lee. There was no reason he'd tell you, and the timing might have been wrong. There's no way to know, you tell Peter.

"And," you say, "they're all dead. Ogan's dead, Puleston's dead, Lee's dead, and Lt. Joyce is dead." You almost say "and I alone survive to tell the tale," but that phrase doesn't sound right, and it doesn't strike the right note, anyway. Too many people are dead; why call attention to your survival?

A couple of days later, you're glad you said nothing. A quick search brings up "And I only am escaped alone to tell thee," from *Moby-Dick*. Then you learn that Melville picked that up from the Book of Job.

# Acting Out

In the interview room you act out the murder. You push away from the table, stand up. Go to the center of the interview room. Begin stage-managing. Pointing at things.

Here's the door, here's the dresser with the turtle tank on it, here's where they were standing.

There was an argument and he struck her.

Here's where he struck her in the forehead with the handaxe and—pointing to the floor—here's where the lunate bloodstain was, showing that she fell and bled on the rug, probably stunned.

Then he picked her up and got her to the bed, over there where you're sitting, laid her on her stomach and beat in her skull.

Then he covered her with the robe, the rug. A burial. Stratified, like an archaeological site.

It's a set piece. How many times have you performed it?

In the Grand Jury chamber, when you'd asked to step away from the witness box so that you could demonstrate what you believed had happened, and the DA had allowed it.

For Becky, in your living room.

In your head, more times than you can count.

You're thinking, *I'm doing the same goddam thing because it's what I think happened,* and you think, *Is this going to make him think I was actually there and if I was actually there then I'm the killer, except I know I'm not.*

And you catch yourself a little bit, catch yourself thinking you're on good terms with him, maybe sort of friends, two guys in a room trying out different scenarios, doing something interesting. But might it be that Peter is thinking, *This guy knows more than he's saying?*

He asks you about the hand ax. Do you think he brought it, or was it already there?

You think it was there, in the turtle tank, and he saw it and grabbed it and used it.

Importantly, you point out, by the time you and Jill found it, it had been washed. Very suspicious, considering that everything else in the turtle tank was filthy and algae-covered. You can't understand how the Cambridge detectives missed something so obvious, you say.

Peter doesn't comment on that. Back in 1969, word had worked its way to you that the Cambridge cops had fucked up, big time. Lost or destroyed evidence. Failed to interview potential suspects. And that by the time the State Police had taken over the case, it was a lost cause.

Again you complain about how the Cambridge guys hadn't noticed it. Too bad you didn't know that a few days later Peter would give you a good insult to use on a loser force: "Mayberry RFD." That would have been better than what you called them, which was "inept."

He asks you about the ochre, and you say that you think it was thrown "like this," probably to help her into the next world, something only an archaeologist would do. Remorseful, or drunk and high, he improvised a death ceremony. The layers of clothing, the rug, stratified the way an archaeological site would be. The killing screamed *an archaeologist did this.*

You were directly responsible for the ochre commotion. One afternoon when you and Jill were in Jane's apartment feeding the turtle, you noticed that what looked like red ochre had been thrown around the room. There were flecks on the wall behind the bed, on the ceiling, but nowhere else. Even undergraduates knew about ochre burials.

You called the Mayberry RFD headquarters and because Detective Dickhead wasn't in, you left a message, which must have immediately leaked, because the evening newscasts were filled with "Ritual Murder" stories, which the powers at the Peabody Museum strongly denied.

All you did was call in something you'd found, but that made the Museum Director in effect call you a liar. He never even bothered to ask you about it. The reflexive denial still angers you, not just because it was insulting, but because it implied an archaeologist was being protected.

You run the *being protected* thing by Peter, who doubts it. He says that stuff like that doesn't happen, not really. You say, "But they let him go to his fieldwork site before he was scheduled to," and Peter says "If we liked him, we would have charged him and taken his passport." And, he continued, they knew they'd be able to interview him when he returned.

You didn't say what you'd thought at the time, which was that Lee would have had plenty of time to work on his story, his explanation, his alibi. You didn't learn until you were already thousands of miles away in the village that he'd managed to alibi himself. And when you did learn it—from a letter Jill's sister wrote you—you dismissed it. Easy to get somebody to lie for you. And, in truth, when you ran into that letter and were scanning it for Becky you thought the same thing. *A bullshit alibi*, you thought, *an alibi of convenience, an alibi from his beard.*

"Back to the ochre," Peter asks, "where did it come from?" and as he asks this you realize that, again, there's something you haven't thought about carefully enough.

He gently points out the inconsistency: you've already said you believed that he hadn't come over meaning to kill her. If it wasn't premeditated, why would he bring ochre?

You're silent. You have no answer. You feel stupid. You've been hanging on to this inconsistency for nearly fifty years without recognizing it. You'd never thought that Lee, in his apartment on the other side of Cambridge Common, had said to himself something like, *I'll grab some ochre before going over to Jane's.* But that's what you've been arguing. It makes no sense.

Your general theory can survive if you ignore the ochre, but ignoring it means tossing out something you've believed all these years, that it wasn't premeditated.

Nobody knows whether Jane had red ochre in her apartment although, as a painter, she might have.

Certain things are disassembling themselves in your head.

*I think there was an argument and he struck her* doesn't fit *He went there meaning to kill her.* You're shaken. Your voice in

131

the recording doesn't change, because at least outwardly you're in *Shit, another thing I didn't think carefully about* mode, but inwardly you're in *I've made a mistake that might cause me trouble* mode.

What might it mean to Peter that you've just fumbled intent?

You don't think you've done anything dangerous, but once again, logic and perhaps memory have failed you. And that doesn't feel good. You told Becky you intended to be *supple*. So much for that. You sense that Peter might have turned you, all knowingly, skillfully, doing what he knows best how to do. Turned you in what way? You realize that you no longer care. It's fine. Whatever.

# Falsely Accused

LATE IN THE INTERVIEW, Peter begins reading names and asking what you know about them. Every name but one's been a Harvard student or faculty member. You've recognized them all, which is not to say you remember them all equally well.

He speaks a man's name and follows it with "a tip?"

There's a small flash of recognition. You've heard that name somewhere, but it triggers no memory. Neither does *tip*.

Peter's list of names has been lying openly on the table. He's been making no attempt to hide it. Just as he's asking about that guy, you look down at it, and you see a name you recognize: your third wife. You think, *Mary? What the fuck? Why is her name on his list?*

You go straight to the same place you were in when you saw Jane's body—your eyes see something, your brain registers it, but you're frozen in *What? What?* You're looking at something you shouldn't be seeing. It's been 13 years since you divorced her.

By the time he asks if you know her, you're able to respond.

"Yeah...I was married to her. How did she get in this?"

"What were the circumstances of the divorce? Amicable?"

You're not tracking his question because your mind's racing to figure out what the hell's going on. "Who's Peter What's-his-name?"

"Someone who gave a tip. So you were married to Mary?"

Oh. "Tip" meant *tip*, as in *tip line*. Diming. Accusing someone of a crime. "Yeah. This is interesting"—a long pause, during which you try to comprehend the enormity of what seems to have happened, which is that someone connected with your ex-wife dimed you for murder— "and horrifying. Mary was my third wife. Not long after I met her, maybe 1995, I told her, this thing happened a long time ago, and I think about it a lot. I probably didn't mention it again, but maybe I did, who knows?"

You spread your arms, palms up, a what the fuck gesture. Shake your head.

Peter shakes his. "Because I'll tell you, this tip isn't ringing my bell. I'm going to say you told her about a murder and she tells this guy about a murder and he goes, 'Oh my gosh, she's married to this guy involved in a murder and he must be the murderer.'"

Amazing. You thought you might be knocked off-balance by something Peter sneaked in to trap you, or accuse you of. But you never imagined sitting there and being told that somebody connected with your third wife had called a tip line about you.

You say, "Unbelievable. When we're getting divorced I learn she's going around saying, 'You know, he was involved in a murder' and 'he was almost indicted for it.'"

You remember calling her on that, and she said "You never told me you didn't do it," to which you replied "I didn't think I needed to!" You realized how profoundly, disastrously wrong you'd been about her character.

You stop for a moment. Peter looks at you and shrugs his shoulders.

## Almost Indicted?

You're still slowly shaking your head in puzzlement. No, *bewilderment*. How had what you told Mary about Jane's murder made its way to somebody you don't know, and how could that guy ever have thought it was worth picking up a phone and calling a tip line in another state?

Maybe that Grand Jury thing was the driver. You decide to ask Peter about it. Maybe he can find out something for you. You tell him the story.

A fellow grad student and his wife, you say, were friends with a guy on the Grand Jury, and *they* told *you* that *he* told *them* that the DA had pushed to indict you. But obviously it never happened. You think about making that joke about how a DA can get a Grand Jury to indict a ham sandwich, but you only say that what he brought must have been weak. For all these years you've wanted to know what they thought they had on you.

Peter spends time talking about how a Grand Jury works, which makes you realize you hadn't fully understood what it was all about.

Eventually you ask him flat out: "What was it?"

"Nothing," he says, "the Grand Jury never went past the investigatory phase. There never was talk of an indictment."

Wait. What? Can this be? The thing that really did frighten you the most back in April, the thing that implied dark forces working in the background—*that thing never happened*? Your worry about what they thought they'd had was unwarranted? But you don't want to put it like that, so you say, "You mean I've been fussing about this fifty years for no reason?" and he says, "Yep. Never happened."

You're dizzy. It hasn't been ten minutes since you learned that Mary engineered a false accusation from something you told her that you believed was true. Then a couple of minutes after you learned *that*, you learned that what you told her was itself false.

*This is fucked up*, you think. Then you say it, and Peter makes a noise of assent.

You get up and walk around the interview room. "What the fuck," you say, "What the fuck!"

Peter starts putting his things away. "It happens," he says, "this kind of shit happens. Don't worry about it."

You're getting angry. You *know* what you were told; nobody forgets anything that shocking. *They tried to indict you.* Jill heard the same thing. She wondered too.

You led Becky to the guy who told you, and then he led her to the Grand Juror. She's talked to both of them. You could ask her what they told her, but you won't, because your understanding with her is that you don't ask her what other people have said.

You sit back down at the table and start uploading the interview. While you're waiting, you make small talk about Hilo, about the volcanoes, about how the Hilo cops use their own cars, so if you don't spot the small blue light on that Toyota Camry behind you, you don't know it's a cop, until it goes on and you're busted. You tell him your high school girlfriend was a cop's daughter, and you used to drive around in his cop car, but she wasn't allowed to turn on the flashers or siren. Peter laughs at that and says, "And?" and you grin and say "Rarely."

You ask him how come you never heard anything about being dimed. "The tip line people got your ex-wife's name, and called her,' he says, "realized right away it was divorce revenge. They see a lot of that."

"Know what she said?" you ask, because it's like the Grand Jury thing. What could she have possibly offered up against you? He says "Don't worry, it wasn't shit."

Then he says, "Hey, your guys busted my balls yesterday," and you say, "We're suspicious of outsiders here, like in Southie," and he says, "Huh, Dorchester," and you both laugh. His *your guys* makes you feel better.

After shaking hands with the Hilo detectives whose room you've been using, you both leave. Peter tells you he's headed for the other side of the island. The resort area. You don't give him a hard time about it.

## After the Interview

BACK IN YOUR CAR, you text Becky: "All good. I'll call within the hour. I talked a lot." It's already dinnertime in New York.

You drive up the hill to your house, still fuming about the diming. The other things you learned—what you got wrong, what you had to reassess, how you felt stupid about the ochre—these were unimportant. They had to do with you and Peter and your memory. You know you're going to be chewing on the being wrong business, but in the car that's not bothering you.

When you tell Ruth about what Mary did, she explodes. "What kind of person would do a thing like that? I'll fly to Buffalo and tear the bitch's eyes out."

You laugh, feeling better.

Ruth will make sure that everybody in Buffalo knows about this.

You think about sending Mary that part of the recording, without comment. You go to your room, fire up an audio editor and extract the part of the interview that begins with the boyfriend's name into a 5 minute long clip. You sit there, thinking about emailing it. It's dinner time in Buffalo. That ought to spoil her dinner, you think. You start the email and then decide to wait.

You go to Ruth and tell her about the clip you just made. You say, "I don't know who the fuck this prick who dimed me is."

Ruth thinks for a moment and remembers hearing from Mary's son that he was her boyfriend after the divorce. That rings a bell with you. That explains the flash of recognition.

You text Becky, "The fucker who dimed me is one of Mary's boyfriends after the divorce. I'd bet anything that she put him up to it."

Becky replies, "I'll grab his address, you take those shark tooth tools."

Yeah. That's just the thing. Grab those nasty replica Hawaiian weapons and fly to Buffalo. Becky can meet you there and the two of you will…will what? Doesn't matter. It's the thought that counts, the vision. Don and Becky, the savage detectives, working over the liar.

Except he's not the important one. Maybe he only swallowed a lie Mary told him, and vomited it up to the MSP.

You're still angry, but at the same time you're very pleased that Ruth and Becky have your back. Ruth always does, but now she's got help. And you're already liking the notion that Mary and her boyfriend had no idea you'd end up knowing what they'd done.

Ruth remembers that the guy taught at Buff State, so you go to the Buff State site and sure enough, there he is. Education. *I should have known,* you think, *a fucking education professor, a dumb shit like the rest of them.* You know that's unfair but really, what the fuck? You don't even know this prick and he called up the Massachusetts State Police Tip

Line and dimed you, and for what? Why? Because your ex-wife asked him to?

Why didn't she do it herself? Oh, yeah. She's a coward. Maybe she told him about it, maybe she lied about you, or maybe he amplified it, and to show her how helpful he was, or to get her into bed, he called it in? A gift? There's no way to know.

The next day you run the false accusation past your friend Stefan, who counsels letting it go, and so does your friend Irving. You call Becky who agrees, saying, "She's not worth it," so you decide not to send the clip. You go to Ruth and tell her, adding "The truth is, they're just pathetic, those two," and she adds "Not too bright, for sure," and you laugh.

# The Murder Weapon?

Two days later you were out on a half-marathon walk when Peter texted from the other side of the island, asking you about the best way to get back to Hilo. You suggested the Saddle Road and offered to meet him half-way and take him to the top of Mauna Kea. This was partly because it's what you do for visitors, and partly because you were hoping to talk to him about the case again.

You're sitting in your Toyota 4Runner in a parking lot on a beautiful but windy day in the Saddle. While you're waiting for him, you and Becky exchange texts—what you could ask him, what he might want to talk about, what she knows that you might pass along without compromising her.

Peter parks his car next to the 4Runner and gets out. Back at the police station he put the DNA kit in his backpack. You tell him that sometimes cars in the parking lot are broken into. "All this way for my DNA, you don't want to be telling your DA it got stolen." He chuckles but grabs the backpack.

And you head up the mountain. You're going to climb 6,000' in 12 miles. This kind of thing is why you and Ruth got the 4Runner.

On the way—taking a cue from Becky—you ask if he could get you the transcript of your interviews with the police. He says he'll ask the DA. In Hilo he'd said your interviews were clear, the best of all of them, to the point and precise, and that he felt he was seeing the scene through your eyes. You thought it was flattery, that he was doing a detective number on you. Even so, you liked hearing it.

You ask him if he knows where the handaxe is. He doesn't.

A few minutes later, he tells you that he bought a pineapple-shaped ashtray for his Prosecuting Attorney, "because of the ashtray," you think he says. That takes you a moment to process. Because you can't think of any reason why he'd tell you about buying a souvenir you conclude it was a coded message. *Ah, Jane's ashtray*, the old heavy square glass kind with sharp corners. And you think, *Ah, the murder weapon then, and the killer's DNA was lifted from it.*

Is he giving you a big hint? If so, what does he think you might do with it? Is he running one of those canary trap operations? Leaking something and waiting to see where it turns up? Back in the interview room he'd said "I don't want to see this in the *Globe*," and you'd said "You won't," but that didn't cover Becky. If he'd said "Don't tell that woman who's writing a book," you're pretty sure you'd have said yes and then told Becky anyway.

You think *Why can't you just say what you're thinking?* but you know the answer: because that's not how it's done. He's not your buddy. You're not his confidant. He's going to tell you what he wants you to know, and nothing else. He's probably alert to the possibility that you'll reveal something significant. That's how it is.

Oh. Wait. That flicker of fear again. You smoked an occasional cigarette in those days. It wouldn't be a surprise if your DNA was on the ash tray. And what then?

When you tell Becky what you're thinking about the ashtray she replies "That's gotta be it."

# KNOCKING AROUND ON MAUNA KEA

PETER TELLS YOU HE DOESN'T LIKE HEIGHTS, so if you notice that he's not looking out the window at the spectacular views, that's why.

You've been on this steep mostly-unpaved road so many times that you don't need to think about the dangerous spots, except for a shortcut down behind the Keck domes at about 13,000' where the road's narrow, soft cinder, no guardrail, and a very wrong move could send you tumbling down a steep slope, rolling, rolling until you fetch up half a mile downslope.

You remember the time you were showing around a guy you'd just met, and when you headed down that road he cried out "I have two little kids!"

Talking with Ruth, after you got back from the mountain, you admitted briefly considering swerving a bit when you got to that stretch, just to jerk Peter's chain. To put a little fear into him, the way you'd been frightened back in 1969, or before he came. That thought was immediately followed by *That would be a dick move*, because for one thing, you liked him by then, for another, he'd treated you with respect. And you don't do dick things to people you like.

The longer the two of you drive around, the more his speech becomes laced with curse words, as yours does, a thing that began in the interview room. It's clearly natural, not something put on to signal closeness. You think this means that he's relaxing, that he really is interested in knocking around Mauna Kea with you, and that he's not setting you up.

In the interview room at the police station when you described yourself as a frightened graduate student, he said you didn't sound frightened to him in the recordings. Oh. Really? That makes you question what you've been feeling since his phone call.

Has the 74-year-old you *invented* the frightened 25 year old? And if so, why?

Have you been amping things up, juicing your narrative, making a better story here on the island and among your mainland friends, including Becky? "Oh, I was scared shitless—that's how bad it was."

Pretending to have been somebody you weren't?

No. Maybe the cops hadn't frightened you in the interview rooms as much as you're remembering, but what leaked out of the Grand Jury had. Except now you know that was some kind of mistake. Or shibai. But in service of what? Why did your friends pass that wrong information on to you? Makes no sense.

You can't pick through this mess while driving on moderately dangerous roads. And you are having a good time, so on the tricky part you drive carefully and slowly. Both hands on the wheel. You don't tell him about the guy who cried for his kids. You don't tell him anything on that stretch except to point out the Subaru observatory and tell him it has nothing to do with the car company.

146

When you point, he says "Keep your hands on the wheel!" You laugh, and so does he.

On the way down you swap stories about your dead mothers and the houses they'd left each of you, you talk about four-wheeling on sand, and getting stuck, he tells some hilarious detective stories, and you show him where you'd buried your parents' ashes.

Then you get back to business.

You've decided to abandon any pretense of not working closely with Becky. You tell him that you spent six days with her. Out in the open, it doesn't seem to bother him.

You tell him that back in 1969 there was talk of the FBI's being involved. You tell him that Becky's wondering whether its interest had to do with some possible spy action at the Iranian site where Jane worked the summer before she was killed, or maybe even antiquity smuggling. She's learned that a metallurgical survey team led by a man who had trained with the OSS visited the site, stayed for a few days and then left.

When she told you that, you thought, *Good cover,* and then you thought, *Indiana Jones, right,* and laughed at yourself. But why the FBI?

Peter's noncommittal but doesn't deny the FBI's involvement.

You tell him the plot of the novel you're writing, how Elliot, the protagonist, would be getting a letter from Kate, the Jane character, with information about what Eric, the Lee character, had done to her. The letter would lead any detective to lean hard on Eric, but that, having been sent to Bougainville and its return delayed for weeks, it arrived back in Cambridge after she was killed.

147

"Wouldn't do any good," he says, because testimony from a dead person isn't admissible. The accused can't question the accuser. You're not even supposed to use something like that in interrogation. You say "So Elliot's going to have to kill him," and Peter says, with what to your ear sounds like approval, "Yeah, revenge."

You're struck by the unreality of it all. You're talking with the detective who's trying to solve a cold case you were involved in half a century before, a case in which you may or may not actually have been a suspect (even now, perhaps?) and you're driving him around at high altitude on rough roads while talking about a fictionalized version of the murder, in which he seems to be approving a revenge killing.

*Holy shit*, you think, *this is weird*. It pleases you.

You ask him if he's going to get DNA from Jim, Jane's boyfriend. He says if he can learn where Jim is, he'll take a trip to get DNA. You tell him you don't know where Jim is, beyond "around Toronto," and you tell him what he already knows, that Andrea, who was in Iran with Jane, but not in Cambridge when she was killed, knows his phone number and address and refuses to give it up. You tell him what Ruth said, that Jim's friends seem to think him a snowflake who needs protecting. He laughs.

You don't tell him that Becky has Jim's phone number. You only know that she has it; you don't know whether she's tried to call him.

You complain about people like Jill and Andrea and some others, who don't want to help. You know this, you say, because they won't talk to Becky. He says that a problem with cold cases is that people say "I'm over that," and they mean it. They get tired of it and want nothing to do with it. They just don't want to talk about it.

You tell him to could expect an email from Alyssa with what she knows about Lee.

Although you hadn't planned it, you realize that on the way down you've been making a move of your own: make sure he knows there's a network of people working on the case and that you're with them. Yes, they're amateurs but they've already shown their power by forcing the DNA work. You're not a solitary guy way out in the middle of the ocean. You don't expect him to say anything like "Let's all work on this together," but you wish he would.

You ask him what would happen if DNA pointed to Lee and he says it would be a political decision but he guesses there wouldn't be an announcement because it's like the letter from the dead girl. Lee isn't alive to defend himself, so you probably don't go public. Boyd would be told first and, turning to you, he says "Then we'd tell you."

That doesn't feel like shibai.

# Going Home

BACK AT THE PARKING LOT you hand Peter his backpack, thinking *Well, there it goes.*

After you shake hands, you give him a copy of your book. He asks you to autograph it, and you do.

He takes out his iPhone, saying, "They're gonna want to know what you look like now."

"Older," you say, "I'm older."

You both stand there in the wind. Looking around. You never tire of the view from this place, but that's not what's keeping you there. The visit seems over, but you're not ready to let it go. You say, "I want to know how you feel about all this. Do you think there's some chance of a resolution? Is it possible?"

"I'm hopeful," he says, "My DA's on fire. It's possible, it's always possible." At that moment you want to believe him, so you do. You don't want to think about shibai. You know what you got is all you're going to get.

You drive down the mountain to Hilo. He's right behind you until it's time for you to turn off into Lower Pi'ihonua. You raise a hand. Maybe he sees you do it, maybe he doesn't.

It's already late in New York, so you don't call Becky. You write up an account of the trip and email it to her.

Over the next few weeks, some texts from him arrive, an email. In August he texts you a picture and asks if you think it's Jim, and you do. You comment that he looks like a sour old guy but when you knew him, he "had a pleasant disposition." The picture looks like man who's had a hard life, and Peter replies "we can't all weather life on an island in paradise." You remind him you lived in Buffalo for more than thirty years and then, because football season's not far away, you add that for some of those years, the Bills *owned* the Pats, and he replies "You have the ADA in hysterical laughing right now."

So, you think, it's all good. You liked that he asked you about the picture. We're working on the case and we're joking, too.

You send the text exchange to Becky, as always.

And yet you do wonder: why the difficulties in finding Jim? And that makes you remember how, in that first phone call, he told you he'd had trouble finding you. "The police had nothing on you," he said. But you have a driver's license with a Hilo address, you own real estate, you pay State taxes, your Facebook profile says you live in Hilo and studied anthropology at Harvard, he knew where Jill was and she would have told him where you were…it makes no sense. It does make you a little uneasy, on the assumption that you are easy to find even for an amateur, much less a non-Mayberry RFD detective. Becky had no trouble locating you back in 2014. What's he hiding?

You email him a few more times, asking him what he thinks about your novel's plot. He doesn't answer. As you get into September, and then October and nothing's happened, you decide that his visit, the interviews, the closeness—it was shibai, after all. It's discouraging. You're not angry at him, but you're disappointed. You'd put a lot of energy into everything, hoping that it would lead somewhere, but it looks as though it hasn't.

You no longer think, or even hope, that Jane's murder's going to be solved. All that's left will be telling her story, which is in Becky's hands and, in a way you don't care to examine closely, may be in Jane's, too.

And then there's *your* Jane story, the novel you'd begun writing before the emails, the calls, the texts, the visits. You can spin that out any way you want. Before Becky and the renewed Jane, you expected to write it alone. Now, maybe, you'll have company.

# GASLIGHTED

AFTER PETER LEFT and you tried to get your life back to normal, the *tried to indict you* business still bothered you. You'd learned that it was false. But what did your friends Paul and Sally think they'd heard from their friend Richie? Had he been explicit? From what Peter said, that couldn't have been true unless he was lying. And why would he have done that? You didn't even know him. It had to have been a misunderstanding, and you wanted to know how it had happened.

It had been more than thirty years since you'd spoken to either of them. When you and Jill divorced, they chose sides, so there'd been no communication.

You composed an email in which you talked about Peter's visit, and about how the Grand Jury thing seemed to have generated a false accusation. You wrote that Peter "wanted to learn what I knew about how that might have happened." You wrote that for many years you'd carried around what they told you, and you'd like to know how it got started.

You were expecting an explanation. But no. Instead, they replied that Richie "never told us about suspects, indictments, or any other part of their deliberations because he was sworn to secrecy…we could not have told you anything."

*Holy shit*, you said to yourself, *they're telling me I'm the one who got it wrong.* You weren't expecting to be gaslighted, but there it was. You couldn't see any other interpretation.

You replied that their assertion that it never happened left you "needing to blame myself—that I must have invented the 'they tried to indict me but failed' thing… and carried that around for all these years." You hoped that "needing to blame myself" would be read as "what the fuck are you talking about?"

This angered you, because it was so completely unnecessary. Why waste time gaslighting an old friend who simply wanted to know the origin of a misunderstanding?

While gathering material for Becky, you'd found and scanned a letter from them, which you hadn't mentioned in your first email, just as you hadn't mentioned that you knew that Becky had talked to them, and to Richie.

Part of the letter described Sally's time with the Grand Jury. She wrote, "Lee was also there…Richie reports that after listening to Lee they are left with a lot of evidence but no prime suspect, no one to pin it on. He wouldn't say any more than that but I guess it means that Lee has cleared himself."

So much for secrecy. You decided to sit tight and see if they responded to your second email. Maybe they'd walk back what they said. But no email arrived.

After about a month you wrote to them, telling them you were working on a non-fiction piece about Jane, and attaching the scanned letter. You thought it would be only fair to warn them you had something in the works. You saw your email as giving them another chance to walk it back, considering that their claim of secrecy was shredded. They didn't take it, instead emailing "We look forward to your piece on Jane."

*Doubling down*, you said to yourself.

Then you sent the entire exchange to Becky.

In 2020 you were thinking about them again, still trying to understand why they'd gaslighted you. It made no sense. All they did was pass along something they'd heard, which was unfortunate but nothing more. You went back and looked at your email.

And you see it. A careless reader could have been put on high alert by "wanted to learn what I knew about how that might have happened." They must have thought Peter was talking about the Grand Jury leak, about how it happened that they knew, or thought they knew, what had happened in the jury room.

But you were writing about Peter's wanting to know how it came about that Mary got somebody to dime you, and where *she* got "almost indicted." He wasn't interested in Paul or Sally or Richie. All he said about Richie was, "I think they heard your name within the thing and it got stretched."

*Yeah*, you say to yourself, *that's it*. Gaslighting you was all about protecting Richie from an imagined threat. What a waste of everybody's time.

More shibai.

# Plotting

IN 2015 YOU DECIDED—for the second time—to write a novel about Jane's murder, but you didn't want to write a novel in which a mid-20s grad student gets into a jam and gets out of it. When you were 25 years old and caught up in a murder, you did not behave in interesting ways. No, you were not much more than a nervous and grieving graduate student, doing your best against the media, the people who believed you were a killer, and of course the cops.

You didn't want to write a mystery or a thriller. You were, as you had been in the past, meaning to write another kind of literary ethnography, in which the ethnographer returns from fieldwork a changed man— because of what he's learned and internalized—and deals with the dissonance between his old culture, and the new one he's learned.

What separates Elliot from the thousands of fictional white men in their 20s, is that Elliot is carrying around in his head two markedly different cultures, with their different prescriptions for proper behavior, ways of looking at the world, even food preferences. You had a lot of fun writing Elliot's search for tinned mackerel in Harvard Square.

When Elliot returns, he's more Nagovisi than American, because of how recently he's been immersed in that culture. When he hits Logan Airport and Kate picks him up, he's only a week out of his ten-household village. The culture shock is massive. He hasn't had a sexual relationship for two years, and he immediately begins one with Kate. Then, before he gets his bearings, Kate's killed and he falls into the hands of the police and media. He works out who killed Kate—an archaeologist named Eric—and, when it looks as though the police can or will do nothing, plans his revenge. It's at this point he begins to use what Mesiamo taught him about violence.

To make this believable, you thought, you'd need the Cambridge events to unfold quickly: two weeks, or three at the most. Thinking back to your own re-entry into the Harvard graduate student world, you remember that within a few weeks you felt at home again. But before that, you were constantly surprised and sometimes thrown off balance by what you encountered in Cambridge. It seemed a world that made no sense to you.

Mesiamo begins the novel with a line that came to you when you were on a 28 mile walk up the Saddle Road and back. Heading home, you ran the line over and over again in your head, deciding between "to kill people" and "about killing people."

I am the one who taught White Man about killing people.

I am the one who killed people when that was the best thing to do—sometimes to solve a troublesome problem, and sometimes to keep a problem from becoming troublesome.

I taught him about killing in the same way
I taught him about language. Sometimes you
speak your mind plainly, because that's the right
thing. Nothing complicated, nothing subtle,
nothing obscure. I've killed people in the same
way. Killing that person was the best solution,
so I did it quickly with whatever weapon I had,
hiding nothing. Other times, you speak indirectly
in ways that some people won't understand, or
that you know they'll interpret in many different
ways, which is just as good. And sometimes you
kill people indirectly, perhaps by forcing them
into situations where they'll die without your
assistance, or you trick someone else into killing
them, or best of all, you reach your goal by not
killing them, while leaving them thinking that at
any time, you might.

When White Man left us to go back to
America, he carried with him everything I'd
taught him. I never trained him to fight or use
weapons. I never expected him to be faced with
the choice of whether to kill someone or not,
nevermind whether to do it straightaway or in
a subtle manner. And yet that did happen, and
when it did, he might as well have had a sack of
weapons and the skills to use them. He behaved
admirably. I'm proud of him, unless he's been
lying to me, which I don't think he has been.

You let the novel drop because you decide to write a
creative nonfiction piece called "Shibai," and send it out
to a contest. That keeps you busy for a couple of months.

Your piece is rejected without comment, although
Becky admires it, saying "This feels like the other half of

mine/how I imagine mine. Which makes perfect sense. But yours is so beautifully realized. I'm honored by the way you portray me."

You couldn't get the novel working. The part set in Nagovisi was easy; you'd already written most of it when you were writing *News of Elsewhere*. The part set in Cambridge was more difficult, because you needed not only a killer and a motive—which you thought you could create from your theory of the real crime—but also a way to have Elliot kill Eric, and get away with it. That was more difficult and, although it was satisfying, it drew you more into classic mystery or thriller territory than you wanted to be.

You'd already gotten Elliot into a relationship with Kate, and you'd figured out how Elliot kills Eric, which is subtle and very Mesiamo-like. So that was in place. But why does Eric kill Kate? Years ago, spurred by the *every bad thing* conversation, you'd decided that Lee killed Jane. When you began plotting Kate's murder you brought that over without examining it closely.

Your time with Sgt. Sennott made you reconsider.

You didn't think you'd convinced him that Jane might have blackmailed Lee. You had only vague ideas about what she might have blackmailed him about; you never saw anything and she never talked about anything. And you couldn't explain *how* Lee could have helped her with her comps. You had no good reason why he should have come after her the night before the comps. Or what they could have argued about, so late in the game. You didn't have much at all.

Sitting at your computer one day, you realized the scenario you'd created was so badly flawed it wouldn't even pass muster as fiction, unless you were willing to ignore everything you knew about how the Anthropology Department and the Museum worked, and give Eric a position that would both give him the chance to reveal the questions or influence the grading, and to do so without being caught. No single professor would grade all the comps, or be able to ensure he graded Kate's. Never.

You did tell yourself that after all it was fiction, but by then you'd read and been disgusted by too many novels that trampled on reality presumably in the belief that most readers wouldn't notice. And you weren't about to transfer the whole thing to East Jesus State University, where you could assert anything you wanted. No, it had to be Harvard. There was no way you could simply assert that Kate somehow forced Eric to agree to fraudulently pass her, and you couldn't build anything plausible. And that spilled over from your fictional world into the real world of Jane, Peter, and Lee. Or perhaps it was the other way around.

You hated to admit that it was only when you started plotting a novel that you saw the flaws in your theory of the crime, but there it was. For all those years you hadn't questioned it. Had you been laying down your own shibai, in the Japanese sense, creating all the roles in your own drama, crafting the narrative *you* wanted? You began to see the outlines of that drama. And having done that, began bullshitting yourself in the Hawai'i sense? And worse, was it—had it been—obvious?

But it didn't make you stop believing that Lee killed Jane. Even though your notions of motive and even action had been undermined, you clung to that. And you remembered that, the year before, Jill had written "I'm sure he killed her, but I don't know why," so you weren't the only one.

When you told Becky your plot, she had no particular comment. Peter only commented on the revenge, not the reason for the killing.

Had Becky begun to think you a fabulist, an amateur, or, worse, a fool? The nutty uncle who won't shut up about UFOs?

To Peter, were you now the Mayberry RFD?

You knew how important they both were to you: Becky as collaborator, and Peter, though you came to doubt him, as the only possible source of a solution. They were both people who would press on and continue working with you no matter what they thought. They'd swallow it and go on. But the idea that they both might think less of you than they had depressed you.

You felt as though you'd shamed yourself.

If the excitement of the spring and summer before was your zenith, late 2017 was your nadir. All shit, everything. Nothing working. No progress. General malaise. Becky no longer seemed to need anything from you. Except you did send her chocolate mochi, which she loved. So there was that.

One day in December when you were in the Saddle going for 32 miles, the same as you'd done the day after Becky left and you'd been elated, it finally settled in: you had nothing at all. So you picked up the pace because, you said to yourself, *I can still do this.* You were at 7,500', battling a stiff headwind, but you pushed hard the last five miles to where Ruth was waiting for you. At the end, you bent over, hands on thighs. You retched but didn't puke. That, at least, was a victory.

# THIS IS NOT A DRILL

JANUARY, 2018. While high on Mauna Kea near the place Puʻu Lāʻau with Ruth and some friends, you stop at a cabin you used to stay in with your father and his hunting friends.

While you're all standing around or going into the trees to pee, your iPhone flashes a message:

BALLISTIC MISSILE THREAT INBOUND
TO HAWAII.
SEEK IMMEDIATE SHELTER.
THIS IS NOT A DRILL.

You're in that same space you were in when you saw Jane's body: between the time your eyes see something and your brain registers it, and the time you think about it rationally. In that space there's a suspension of belief, then you have to take action.

You think, *Can this possibly be true? North Korea?* You have to process what you know. The phone's not scrolling, so you've seen everything there is to see.

You don't know whether to dismiss it or believe it. It came through the usual warning channel used for eruptions, tsunamis, landslides, flash floods. But missile attacks? Even if one's in progress, you're probably safe because it's Pearl Harbor, 200 miles away, that should be targeted. But...maybe the North Koreans haven't mastered precision aiming. Incoming should mean, what, 10 or 15 minutes max?

You say to Ruth, "This is a good place to die," but you feel silly saying it. If those are your last words, they shouldn't be what people say in films or novels. It's true, though. You've told Ruth that your idea of a good exit would be to sit on Mauna Kea, drop some pills, and go down with the sun.

You call your son in Brooklyn. You think about saying "Goodbye, I love you," but that seems insane, because you don't think there really is a threat. But what's going on, then? He gets to work on the internet seeing what he can find out.

Ruth calls her daughter in LA.

Your friends have no children, so they don't call anybody.

When you get off the phone with your son, feeling as though an attack is very unlikely, you think about who else to call. Becky, of course. But you don't. It would be looking for an answer to a question that you've never asked: are we as close as I think we are?

Back home, probably because you've been thinking about Becky, you compare what you just felt—and did—to that day in January, 1969 when you saw Jane's body, touched her leg, felt the cold skin, went to her head, more cold, blood, blood, death.

How long were you in that space where you saw, and moved, but did not *process*? You mimic your actions and count one Mississippi, two Mississippi...thirteen

Mississippi. So, say fifteen seconds from *Jane lying there* to *She's dead.*

Had you looked at your phone for fifteen seconds, trying to understand? It was probably that long before you turned it to Ruth and said, "Did you get this?"

In both cases you weren't sure what to do next. Both were outside your ken, although with Jane you knew you needed to call the police. That there was nothing you could do about Jane herself was clear to you. At Puʻu Lāʻau you knew that nothing you could do would have any effect on incoming missiles.

The difference was that in Jane's apartment you didn't feel at risk. You didn't feel endangered. That was coming, but you didn't know it then.

At Puʻu Lāʻau you thought you might be in danger, but you didn't know what kind. You never thought you'd be vaporized but you knew—every thoughtful person in Hawaiʻi knew—that if Honolulu were taken out by anything (missile, hurricane, terrorists) the entire state would fail. The outer islands depend on Honolulu for almost everything.

# LIGHTS OUT

YOU NEVER WONDERED about death much, including what might come after it. Even as a boy, the notion of an afterlife seemed very odd, especially on those few times in the Congregational church your family attended when the minister talked about it. You die, except you don't because there's a sky person who saves you. Or you save yourself. Or something. It made no sense, and it makes no sense now.

To you, for years, it's been a topic not worth thinking about because the only answer beyond *lights out* lies in some kind of faith, and that's not a place you inhabit, the world of faith. Of any kind. Being inclusive, you don't believe in reincarnation either, no matter how much Buddhist thought attracts you.

You've killed many living beings, though never a human one. You've looked into a large mammal's eyes, one that the bullet or broadhead had not killed, and finished the job. "Slit its throat," your father said when you were on your knees next to the first sheep you'd shot, a ewe, and so, thinking *slit*, you opened your clasp knife, pulled her head back, and, as you wrote in fiction forty years later, "felt hot breath on my thumb and heard a little bleat, a moan perhaps, rushing air, or a soft doom-sigh." And you cut. Slashed, because it wasn't as easy as you expected. And the blood gushed, painting the knife and your hands, pumped for a moment, dropped to a trickle. And she finished dying.

You gutted her, skinned her, butchered her and put the parts you wanted in a white cotton meat sack, lashed them to your pack board and packed them out. You were probably twelve.

Almost half a century later you worked that into your story "Burials."

Part of it was set at an archaeological site, a dig, involving a narrator who was approximately you, something that happened in the real world of the East Bay in 1963, and something that happened on Mauna Kea years later. When you wrote the story you were thinking about disposing of the dead.

My father said, "Don't bury me. I don't want to be any place when I'm dead."

So when he'd finished dying I climbed up on the mountain to scatter his ashes as I'd long ago promised I would. I went to a place where the wind never stopped, and our mountain spread itself out below me. And when I turned and looked up it seemed to spread out above me too, rather than retreat or diminish.

I took off my clothes and laid them on the ground, and I poured gritty ashes in my hand and I whirled and threw them into the wind, and when I'd whirled and thrown those I whirled and threw some more until they were almost all gone, except those that had blown in my face and my hair, and then I put the rest in my mouth to be with me a little longer.

In college and grad school you came to understand that only one or two of your friends had ever killed anything larger than an insect or a small rodent. You could handle knives and firearms and bows and arrows and had been in high wild places by yourself, even as a teenager. And you understood, at some level, that this set you apart from them.

You had seen—caused—the transition from life to death many times, and they had not.

That never made you feel superior. Or tougher than they were. You did feel that you knew things they didn't know, had experienced things they had not, had looked death in the eye, both as someone to whom potential death had unexpectedly made an appearance and as someone who had caused it.

You never thought that a person who hunted and killed was in any way superior to one who had not, beyond knowing how to do that and, if he paid attention, understanding what was going on. Especially the lights-out part.

You believed that what happened with the sheep, the pheasant, the wild pig, the quail, when the lights went out was a simple thing that needed no theology nor any philosophy either, which is not the same as saying you were unaware of the enormous bodies of thought bearing on that moment and what might happen after it. Lights out does it for you.

And that includes Jane.

# A CRIME OF PASSION

ON ANOTHER DAY, you think about that Mauna Kea hunting cabin's other resonances.

It was where you used to spent the night on hunting trips with your father, his hunting buddy Mr. Yanagihara, and Mr. Yanagihara's son Robert, three years ahead of you at Hilo High. You and Robert were friends outside of school, but—schools being pretty much the same everywhere—not in school. The two of you often hunted independently of your fathers. Once you nearly shot him by accident, blasting a load of birdshot into the ground not far from his foot. You remember thinking *The safety's on* when you put pressure on one of the two triggers. But it wasn't. He was startled but not angry. You were mortified. You didn't tell your fathers.

What came to your mind there at the cabin was that only a few years later, having graduated and moved to Honolulu for work, he strangled a married woman. She had two children. He was quickly caught. Being Japanese, his father was so ashamed he couldn't face your father and so there were no more trips to Puʻu Lāʻau with Mr. Yanagihara.

Robert wrote you a letter from prison, in which he urged you not to make mistakes, as he had. There was some Jesus in it too. You kept that letter for a long time, probably because it connected you to something completely outside your experience: murder. And to a murderer.

Somehow, what you thought about Robert didn't change. You weren't angry or disgusted; you didn't hold him in contempt. You do remember wondering how such a thing could have happened, by which you meant the motive, the sequence, the result.

Perhaps it was because, as a much younger boy, you had become aware that you could think about, you could imagine, anything. Any act, no matter how bad. Nothing mattered if it was in your head. There were no constraints, no consequences. You don't remember the exact day you realized this, but you remember the feeling that everything, literally everything, had opened up for you. You never thought this was anything but an imaginative exercise, perhaps an intellectual one. You were no boy Raskolnikov.

So perhaps it was that in action. Perhaps you kept what Robert had done in your imagination, and perhaps it was because he'd done it in a distant place and you'd never been in his presence afterward. In some way, that transformed his crime into something without consequences, except for him.

You remember thinking *I know a murderer* as if it were the same as knowing an important or famous person. You knew nothing about human death, or dead bodies, because this was before the tsunami. You did know a great deal about animal death, having been its agent many times up on Mauna Kea.

You remember being told that Robert and his victim were having an affair and that he strangled her in her bedroom with a venetian blind cord. You remember being told it was a "crime of passion." Only 15, you didn't understand how passion could lead to murder. The best you could do was by analogy—perhaps she broke up with him, he couldn't stand it, and the murder was something like *If I can't have you, nobody can.*

You don't remember ever judging him, although it's impossible that your mother and father didn't. You can't remember talking about it with them.

Many years later—in 2009—you had written a personal essay for an online magazine in which you talked about hunting on Mauna Kea. You worked him into the essay, murder and all. You decided to look for him, got an email address, and wrote him a short note, to which he replied in a friendly manner. You didn't mention your essay. Of course you didn't mention the murder, or prison. After that, nothing, which was fine with you. You wanted to make contact but that was all.

In 2020 you found someone with his name on Facebook, but decided to let it go. You weren't sure it was him; the face that looked at you from the page was no one you recognized.

In 2019 you were working on the second version of your Jane novel, and he made an appearance there, too. Yes, it was fiction, but you were again curious. You remembered nothing of the newspaper stories. So you went back to the web to see what you could find.

In one of those "look back in time" sections in a Honolulu paper, a reader asked about the murder. To your surprise, a staffer replied that the murder involved a botched robbery attempt. Your reaction was that the newspaper had, for some reason, not looked very carefully into the case.

So you let it drop, because Robert's only role in your novel was to be talked about as your two characters were walking around in the cabin. What really happened in 1958 wasn't important.

But in Fall 2020 you signed up for a newspaper archive service because you couldn't remember the name of the sleazy reporter who misused what you and Jill had told him about Jane. As long as you had access to old newspapers, you thought, why not search for Robert and see where the 2019 report had gone wrong?

It hadn't gone wrong. None of the stories talked about any romantic entanglement. Everything was about the robbery. You were astonished. You remembered nothing about a robbery. Only the venetian blind cord, and the affair.

You were dismayed. Not that you'd forgotten what was in the papers, which were delivered to the house every day and which you must have read. Working with Becky and Peter had made you recognize that you hadn't remembered as much of the distant past as you thought you had, but that wasn't it.

The dismay came from the parallel between Robert's *crime of passion* and the Jane case's *tried to indict*. In both cases you were certain you remembered correctly what you'd been told. It wasn't a matter of having misunderstood. These phrases—and that's the form in which those memories were encoded and stayed with you all these years—didn't just appear. They're not part of everyday speech. They got into your head because somebody spoke them, and you believed them.

*Tried to indict* seems simple to you now: a misunderstanding between Paul or Sally and Richie that was passed along to you. They gaslighted you because they wanted to protect their friend. You don't give a shit any more.

*Crime of passion* doesn't seem as simple. The newspaper accounts seemed unreal to you. Even for fifties journalism they seemed stilted. Robert's actions, as reported, were those of a killer who didn't much care whether he was caught. And when he was caught, he confessed, although later entered a plea of not guilty. The trail he left was easily followed; his alibi was worthless. The venetian blind cord was found in the bathroom next to his rented room. *How could he not have gotten rid of it?* you thought.

The stories talk about killer and victim driving around in her station wagon after she picked him up near where he'd left his car. He was said to have tied a bandanna over his face, but that she recognized him and thought it was joke. He had a knife. He was said to have tried to rob her in the car, but because she had no money with her they went to her house to get it, there was a struggle, and he killed her.

An hour and a half elapsed between the time they went into the house and the time she was killed. What happened during that time? You try to imagine how Robert spent ninety minutes with his victim. Talking? Arguing? Perhaps making a deal: I'll go away, you shut up about this, and no one needs to know? At some point there was a fight. She bit his finger before he killed her, likely as he was strangling her. He tried to pass it off as a dog bite.

What to make of this? The newspaper articles felt *wrong* to you. What if it *was* as simple as what you'd been told—an affair, something went bad, he strangled her, and the robbery business was shibai. You hadn't been the only one who'd heard about an affair: the Honolulu detective chief was quoted in the newspaper as saying there was "definitely no love angle" and that the victim's character was "unimpeachable."

A coverup? But why? She didn't come from an important family, and neither did her husband. There were no political connections, so it was hard to see why those in power would want to protect her reputation. You can imagine a cover-up, but you can't make yourself believe in one.

Far more likely that Robert's Hilo friends and family put out the *crime of passion* story because it reflected better on Robert and his family than armed robbery leading to murder. And you bought into the shibai. It pushed out everything you'd read in the papers, and stayed with you.

There's shibai, and there's shibai, and then there's shibai.

## SHORT TAKES

JANUARY, 2018. You learn from your son that Sgt. Sennott never went to Buffalo to interview Jill and get DNA from her. This strengthens your thinking that everything—the trips, the DNA—was shibai. You feel used, a pawn in some political game being played thousands of miles away in Massachusetts.

February, 2018. You're texting with your son, who needs a compressor. You find a good one on Amazon, copy the link, and carelessly paste it into the text window you've been using for Peter, which was up next to your son's because you've been copying his old texts for Becky.

"Sorry a mistake, meant for my son."

The phone rings almost immediately. It's Peter, who gives you a hard time about the compressor before saying, "By the way, you're cleared."

You think he's telling you that the your DNA didn't match what was on the murder weapon. You're pleased to hear it, but you think, *This is how I learn I'm cleared of murder? An accidental text?*

Then you wonder whether "cleared" implies that you really were a suspect.

You think about posting on Facebook. "Good news! I've been cleared of a 49 year old murder," but both Becky and Ruth counsel against it. You know they're right, so you don't. In the diming clusterfuck they had your back. Now they anchor you.

April, 2018. You're diagnosed with prostate cancer, which requires trips to Honolulu for a CAT scan, MRI, biopsy, and an expensive shot to drive your testosterone to zero, something you'd rather not have happen. Except you'd rather not die, either.

Hot flashes. Weakness. Weight gain. Man boobs. Dramatically-lowered libido. You're ashamed of your body, not just how it looks, but what it can't do for you any longer. Oddly, your training for 75k goes well. And you don't die.

In Honolulu the screen in the biopsy room is showing three pelvic scans. When you're alone, you get off the table and inspect them. One scan is obvious. Ilium, ischium, os pubis, lumbar vertebrae. Femoral heads. The standard landscape.

The other two are disorienting because the view's from inside your abdomen, looking down. Strange and wonderful. A pair of wrinkled objects. Wait. Are those my balls? Holy shit, they are.

You take out your phone and make a picture of the screen, which you send to Ruth and your son.

You think of sending it to Becky. But then you think, *A CAT scan of my balls is mighty like a dick pic.* So you don't. But the thought makes you laugh, which is a good thing when you're about to have an ultrasound wand shoved up your butt and twelve needles shot into your prostate, without anesthetic.

After the biopsy, you sit with a nurse, who goes over the recovery instructions. They're straightforward, you're nodding your head, and then she says "bloody ejaculate for six weeks," which catches your attention. You've had bloody urine and you've had bloody stool but that's it. She catches you raising your eyebrows. "No, really," she says, "and you wouldn't believe the calls I take from guys who don't listen. They say 'I gotta see the doc right away, something's wrong, I got bloody, you know, *stuff*, can you get me in?' and I say, 'No worries. Read the instructions I gave you,' and they say 'You don't understand! Something's really wrong!' It takes me a while to calm them down."

You laugh. You're having trouble imagining what bloody ejaculate might look like. Flecks of blood? Red tint? It amuses you.

"Men!" she says, "Women understand, we have blood coming from everywhere."

On your next visit you tell the urologist he has the best staff ever.

May, 2018. The East Rift Zone of Kilauea Volcano erupts. Twenty miles away, it often sends choking fumes over to Hilo. You lay in new cartridges for your respirators. Earthquakes, including one big one. Ruth, California girl that she is, gets in a doorway. You hang on to your iMac so it doesn't slide off your desk. Ruth scolds you. You'll do better next time. Glow in the sky. Sgt. Sennott texts, wondering whether the eruption is a threat.

You now have zero testosterone. You joke with your women friends—but not Becky, who's too young—about your hot flashes. You monitor your behavior closely. Your emotions. Are there changes? You're not aware of any. Hormone balance and emotions aren't closely-linked, but you did think you'd feel *something*. You're disappointed; it would have been interesting.

Months later it occurs to you that the emotional fragility that came upon you in the late summer and fall might have been hormone-related.

You have only one *I'm gonna die* meltdown.

June, 2018: You cadge a ride on a doors-off helicopter to fly low over the eruption and photograph it. Leaning out the door with two pro Nikons and long lenses around your neck perks you up a bit. Maybe you've still got *something*.

When you land you realize your belts hadn't been clicked in properly. Or maybe they had. All you really know is that when you went to unbuckle, the tongue came out easily. *Not my day to die*, you think, and then you think *Unless I really was buckled in but fumbled the unbuckling.*

An omen? You don't believe in omens. If there's a lesson, it's that there are more uncertainties in the world than you like to admit, buckled or not buckled being one of them. And you can't go back and check.

You go home with a thousand shots. This isn't your first time shooting lava from a helicopter, so you know to use burst mode. Every time you press the shutter you get 6 or 8 shots. It's the only way to do it: you're maneuvering to get your cameras out the open door, the one you're not using is whacking you in the chest, the wind's buffeting you, you don't know which way the pilot's going to fly or at what angle, and the lava's moving too. Carefully compose a shot? No.

Did you buy some Croakies? No, you forgot, just as you forgot the last time you went up doors-off. So you also have to worry about a gust of wind or rotor wash snatching your glasses and sending them down to the flow.

In your daily photographic practice—your daily mindfulness work—you use your Nikon as if it were a view camera, on a tripod, composing the shot on the display screen. In half an hour you might make only two or three shots. Up in the air, it's different: *spray and pray.*

Out of the thousand, fifteen or twenty are very good. You email some to Peter. To Becky. You'll put them up for sale.

July, 2018. When it's time for the 75k walk, you text Becky from 25.5k as usual but, at about 60k, your back goes into spasms. Bent sideways, you scuttle along the shoulder like a land crab. To your surprise, nobody stops. You've seen dozens, if not hundreds, of marathon finishers who've gotten into trouble, so you know what you look like. Don't any of the drivers recognize the signs?

You crab along to age 65 and then, as runners say, you crash and burn. You text Ruth, who's at 75k waiting for you, and she drives back, you get gingerly in the 4Runner, and she drives you home.

You've never failed a birthday walk, so this hurts. Blaming the zero-T seems like a cop-out to you. You don't blame the cancer, either. Same reason. You blame yourself for thoughtlessly increasing your pace when you hit the flats. You should have used that section to recover from the long climb.

You wait two weeks and take another shot. This time your goal is finishing, not self-examination, so you don't text Ruth and you don't text Becky. You make it with no excitement, although at 70k a cop pulls over on the shoulder in front of you and asks if you're all right.

"Somebody called in about you," he says, and you laugh. "Two weeks ago I was in big trouble and nobody stopped. Today I'm fine, 5k to go, no problem." The cop asks, "What are you doing, anyway?" and you tell him you're walking from Hilo. His eyes widen and he smiles. You know he wants to say "Brah, you're crazy," but he doesn't.

On the way back you email everybody on the east coast instead of texting them, because it's after midnight there. Becky texts you the next afternoon. "How are you feeling about it all today?" and you reply, "Got it done. 13:43. Another year down." She replies, "DON! I'm so impressed and deeply happy for you…So inspired by your commitment and perseverance and strength."

The next day you began radiation.

## He Felt Heavy So I Knew He Was Dead

INSTEAD OF USING the second 75k walk for contemplation, you spent time thinking about how Becky would use the material you'd given her. It was curiosity—even amusement—rather than worry that made you wonder.

Because you'd agreed not to share, you could only guess at how she'd handle that material. Would she quote you? Paraphrase? Would she lift passages from letters and quote them? Would she present your commentary on letters you'd written? Would she describe scenes as you talked?

At times you'd been uncomfortable, even uneasy, as you revealed not just what you knew, but yourself. Would she take something you'd said and run it by someone else, for comment, such that another person would comment on something you'd said or done? And then she'd comment on to of that? What a chain!

Would she use the form that the *New York Times* reporter had in 1969, "…offered a visitor a glass of sherry," where the visitor would be Becky? That seemed unlikely. No, impossible. You'd always disliked that form—unnecessary masking, as if the reader were too dense to work out that the journalist was actually in the frame; entirely too cute, in your opinion. Even so, you spent a few minutes imagining some of what happened in your living room in that style. Things got ridiculous very quickly.

What you imagined her doing were standard non-fiction techniques; you'd used them yourself. On a walk that would last 14 hours, your questions helped you pass the time. Part of you hoped she'd go all postmodern or experimental, perhaps taking something you'd reported, perhaps a scene, and rendering it in different ways. The prism thing. You were certain that at least some of what she wrote would be unusual.

This made you think of something you'd sketched out when you were working on the Jane novel that had crashed and burned. You had a page of hand-written notes from 1972 that you'd never transcribed, in which Mesiamo tells you how he went to another village meaning to kill someone, and did.

What stuck in your head—you'd even projected part of that page in that multimedia piece you performed in Buffalo—was when Mesiamo told you "He felt heavy, so I knew he was dead." Mesiamo had stabbed the man to death, but he'd said nothing about blood, nothing about any cries of pain, or moans, no thrashing…just his victim's weight.

After you'd cleared the last nasty uphill stretch—of course looking at your watch and marking 25.5k but not texting Becky—you got the idea of having Elliot retell a story Mesiamo had told him—to Mesiamo. The twist was that Mesiamo did not want Elliot to read back his notes in the order he'd taken them. He wanted him to tell it as a story.

By the time you finished you had much of the story in your head. The next day, after radiation, you wrote it.

One day I was telling White Man about a time when I was nearly killed because I was foolishly daring. I wanted him to see me getting into trouble, and then getting out of it.

When he finished writing I had an idea. I wanted to see whether he understood how it was that I killed people.

I said, "White Man, read me what you wrote. Read me my story."

He said, "I'll say what you spoke," but I said, "No, tell it as though you were telling someone else."

He was quiet for a moment and then began. "If you look near Mesiamo's house in Biroi village, you'll see a large *marimari* tree, which was planted in memory of the fight during which Mesiamo killed Lon-isi."

I said, "It would be a better story if you didn't say I killed Lon-isi at the beginning," and White Man said, "But that's not how you told me about it," and I laughed and said that I wanted him to turn what I'd told him into a story, even perhaps into something that could become a chant, or song.

"Oh," he said, "it doesn't have to be true?"

"It has to be mostly true," I said, "but you don't have to tell it the way I told it to you."

"I see," he said, "good. Let me think."

After a moment he said "I'm ready," and I said, "Tell me."

"Once there was a powerful Big Man called Mesiamo, who had several wives. One of them, Ing, was from a village called Bereteba. She had a

182

bad temper. One day, she began shouting at him, accusing him of only screwing his other wives, never her. 'Did I marry you only to work in your taro gardens?' she yelled, 'do you think a wife is only for raising pigs?'"

I stopped White Man. "She never said that," and he said "You told me to make up a story and you never told me why you and she were fighting."

What could I say except, "Continue?"

"Ing shouted, 'I'm going to Bereteba. My people will send the bride wealth back. Buy a sow with it and then you can fuck that pig as well as your other wives.' She spit on the ground and when she turned to go, Mesiamo kicked her in the ass. Her wrap fell off, and there she was, completely naked. She didn't care. She leaned over and showed him her asshole, as men sometimes did when they were fighting, to show contempt."

"White Man," I said, "that never happened!" and he said, "I know, but it could have and you told me to tell a story."

"Indeed," I said, "indeed." In truth I was trying to keep from laughing. There aren't many of us who would have had the courage to make up a story like that. I was proud of White Man, and I'll tell you why: he understood that when a man like me says "do as you wish," he means it. I was testing White Man but White Man was testing me, too.

"Continue."

"Two days later, a Bereteba woman heard Ing's brothers plotting to kill Mesiamo when he came to Bereteba, as they knew he would. She didn't think that a kick in the ass was worth a killing, so she sent word that he should not to come to Bereteba lest he be attacked."

"That's true," I said.

White Man paused for a moment. Then he looked directly at me, smiled a little smile, and said, "Mesiamo didn't like being warned, because he knew that eventually people would hear about it, and if he didn't go to Bereteba, people would think him afraid. He wished that no one had warned him, because then he could control the situation—either go, or not go."

I was surprised, because I never said that to White Man, nor had I even hinted at it. And yet there it was—and it was true. I was pleased, so I said, "Very good, White Man, very good."

"One morning Mesiamo put his small knife in his wrap, took no other weapon, and headed for Bereteba. He called to the children to come with him, but he didn't take any men."

"That's true," I said.

"When Mesiamo and the children entered Bereteba, there was a man named Kinkara with a bow and arrow. When Kinkara saw Mesiamo he made a motion and one of the young men began beating a slit gong. Mesiamo thought that Kinkara was bluffing, trying to gain time so that his men could come from where they were hiding, called by the drumming. So he approached Kinkara and in a swift move snatched the bow, put it over his knee, and broke it."

"Also true," I said.

"At that time, out of Mesiamo's sight, a man named Lon-isi entered the village, carrying a possum he'd killed in the bush. Not realizing what was happening, Lon-isi hung the possum on the wall, saw what was happening and picked up a kind of spear called *bekosa*. Mesiamo saw none of this—it was happening behind him. He was paying attention to Kinkara, which was foolish because Kinkara had no weapon and was no threat. Mesiamo was pleased by the way he'd overpowered Kinkara, and not paying attention to what was happening behind him."

I said, "It's true, the way you're telling the story. I was careless."

White Man said, "Yes, you were, and I'll continue. Mesiamo was feeling powerful, and was trying to decide whether he should kill Kinkara, or not. He knew he didn't have much time. But foolishly, he concentrated on Kinkara. Lon-isi ran up behind Mesiamo, who was foolishly not paying attention, and struck him on the head. Mesiamo fell to his knees from the blow."

I said, "Perhaps this story could have fewer 'foolishlys' in it. One is enough," and White Man laughed. "All right," he said, "but it was you who said 'foolishly daring.'"

"Yes, but I only said it once, and it was about going to Bereteba with only my small knife and no men, not about having allowed Lon-isi to sneak up on me from behind."

White Man nodded his head. "On his knees, Mesiamo said to himself, 'Whoever hit me isn't a fighter, or I'd be dead,' and, knowing that, got to his feet to see who had struck him. It was Lon-isi, who didn't run away because he knew that if he did, Mesiamo would kill Kinkara."

"That's true," I said, "two men who didn't know how to fight, each protecting the other. I wanted to kill them both but even with a head wound and not thinking too clearly, I admired their courage."

"I'll continue," White Man said. "Mesiamo stood there quickly deciding what to do about these two brave but foolish men who had attacked him. 'Do that again!' he shouted, and Lon-isi tried an overhand strike, which he easily dodged. Had Lon-isi used a sweeping blow, Mesiamo thought, that might have finished him off. But before the second strike, he had moved close to Lon-isi, and thus the *bekosa* hit the ground and flew from his hand. Mesiamo was able to grab it."

"All true," I said. "But don't forget about Lobirate," and White Man gave me a false hard look and said, "This is my story now," which I suppose it was. Even so I wanted to be part of it which, now that I think about it, was a strange thought—wanting to be part of my own story.

"The woman Lobirate ran up to Mesiamo and tried to hit him with a coconut-husking stick, but it fell from her hand. Mesiamo threw the stick on a roof, pushed Lobirate into Kinkara, who fell down, and turned to Lon-isi, who was standing there stupidly, unable to decide what to do."

"Maybe 'confused' instead of 'stupidly,'" I said, "even though I hadn't hit him yet."

"No," White Man said, "I prefer 'stupidly,' because anybody standing near you, weaponless, who didn't run away into the bush would be a stupid man."

I said nothing because I agreed. It's just that I don't like to call people stupid unless they really are. Doing something stupid, which anybody can do, is not the same as being a person with an empty head.

"Continue," I said, "let's hear how you tell the next part."

"Mesiamo held the bekosa loosely in his hand, as though he was going to drop it. With his other hand, he took out his small knife, so that Lon-isi could see it."

"I didn't!"

"You did, and that distracted Lon-isi. He was watching the knife, not the bekosa. Suddenly Mesiamo swung the bekosa upward, Lon-isi failed to react, and it struck him on his jaw, knocking him off balance. Mesiamo threw down the bekosa, caught Lon-isi as he was staggering, turned him around so that he could strike with the knife in his left hand, in the chest and then, as he was falling forward, took the knife in his right hand and stabbed him in the back. Mesiamo put his left arm around Lon-isi. He felt him sag and become heavy, and knew he was dead."

I was surprised. In fact I rushed Lon-isi head-on and stabbed him. White Man's story was better. The way he had me attack Lon-isi was better, though slower. I liked it. White Man was forgetting that I had to end the fight quickly, before the men called from the bush by the slit gongs arrived. Even so, I thought that if I told the story again, I might change that part of the fight, and tell it the way White Man did.

"Continue," I said.

"There's only a little more. A man named Bensai ran towards Mesiamo, trying to shoot arrows while running. These arrows were of the kind called *maga*, barbed with flying fox bones and dipped in shit, so they were dangerous. But no arrow struck Mesiamo, because he was using Lon-isi's body as a shield."

"I dodged them, you know. I had already dropped Lon-isi's body. And you don't need to name the arrows. Everybody knows what they were."

"Yes, but I'm going to tell this story in America, where they don't know one kind of arrow from another. And as for dodging, my story is better because you use one enemy to protect yourself from another," White Man said, "and I wish you'd let me finish my story."

I grunted as if I were annoyed. Of course I wasn't, not at all. Of course he would be telling my story in America. In truth I hadn't stopped to think about that.

"'This is your fault!' Mesiamo shouted to the village, even though everybody—Lobirate, Kinkara, Bensai and the others—had run away into the forest. 'You started it' he shouted, 'you knew what I would do,' and then he put his small knife back in his belt, picked up the bekosa and started back to Biroi. He thought about showing his asshole to them, but there was nobody to see it. And that's the end of my story."

You decide to send the story to Becky. You're sure she'll like it, and she does.

## This Call Never Happened

RADIATION BEGAN the day after the walk: a scheduled eight weeks, five days a week. A few days before, as prep, you were given three small tattoos for aiming the beam. Dots: left hip, midline, right hip. You tell Becky, who says "You're an ellipsis now."

The only tricky part about radiation is that you have to have your bladder filled to a certain level, which they check when you're on the table, and if there's too much pee, you have to get off and go drain some and if there's too little, you have to drink water and wait, which nobody wants. Everybody knows how to empty a bladder, and everybody knows how to fill one up. But to keep it at a specific level takes practice. You don't get it right for a full week.

The technicians—Noa and Lei—are wonderful. If you're too full, they say, "Go pee." On the first day they told you gas in your intestines causes trouble, "so we may call you on the intercom and say 'Fart!'…just do it. No worries."

On the third day, a Wednesday, your phone rings while you're getting zapped. When you're out of the machine you play the message. It's Sgt. Sennott, who says "Just want to talk to you a second. Update you a little." He sounds upbeat.

You text: "Right now I'm in the oncology radiation place but I'll be home 30 mins max and will call. Prostate cancer, ugh."

He replies: "Sucks but beatable. Good Luck. No hurry."

No hurry! *Right,* you think. *After months of silence he wants to talk but there's no hurry? Something's going on.*

You need to strategize with Becky. You text her that you hope he doesn't swear you to silence, "assuming this might be about the perp."

Just in case he does put you under seal, you suggest that she prepare some leading questions to which you'll answer only Yes or No, thus honoring...honoring what? Your word? You remember the post-truth world of the interview room and can't see why *you* shouldn't be the one unbound by truth.

Peter says, "This call never happened."

Your heart rate jumps up. This sounds like the real thing. "Got it."

"There's a break in the case. We have somebody. Announcement Monday."

You ask if he can tell you anything more, and he says, "You didn't trust me that we were working on the case, and I understood. But we were. So trust me."

You text Becky. "Trust me, he said. So wow. The way he talked about it, I'm guessing an announcement from the DA. An embargo of some kind up until then."

And you realize, yes, you *do* trust him.

Becky's in Boston but she's headed to Florida for a wedding. She says she'll catch the first plane back to Boston Monday morning.

All week, you're excited. Who? Who is it? You suspect a couple of people who are still alive, even though you admit to yourself it's only because you dislike them. How sweet if it were one of them.

Thursday you email Becky:

Whatever happens on Monday wouldn't have happened without you, Todd, Michael, and Alyssa. So what I'm hoping you're thinking/feeling is something like *I made this happen.* Yeah, you weren't the only one. But you were and are a major figure in this. What I'm saying is that as I was thinking about how cool and exciting all this is, what popped into my head was, literally, 'Becky made this happen.'"

Sunday you email her, "I can't help thinking that the killer might be someone unknown to all of us, swept up by DNA. If those California cold case folks can do it, why can't the MSP?"

On Monday you're up by four, because Boston's six hours ahead of you. Best to be ready by ten theirs.

Becky tells you she's boarding and goes silent until she lands at Logan.

You write, "I'm so so tempted to call Peter, but I'm resisting. What if this isn't what we think it is?"

She replies, "Oh I think it might well be a private announcement. Especially if the person has passed. Though I find it hard to imagine the DA wouldn't want to leverage it for good press. I'll be attached to my phone."

191

Mid-morning, nothing. You're thinking maybe it's a false alarm. Or a mistake. Peter jumped too soon and has gotten slapped down by his DA.

Becky asks around a little but turns up nothing.

You think about calling Todd at the *Globe*, hinting that something's in the air, and suggesting he check his sources to see if anything's scheduled. *Surely he has sources in the DA's office*, you think. But then you realize you have two good reasons not to do that.

First, it feels like a tease. True, you don't know how these things are done but to you it starts to feel almost *I know something you don't*. And that's chickenshit. Todd treated you fairly when you asked him to change something in the article, and you owe him. When you think about all this more carefully, it doesn't add up, logically. But you're going to go with your gut feeling. You just can't be that guy who says "I know something but I'm not telling." Cannot.

Second, in the interview room at the Hilo station, Peter said "I don't want to read about this in the *Globe*," and you agreed and kept that promise. Only Becky and Ruth know what was talked about in that room, except for the diming. But if Todd pushes aggressively, somebody might hear about it and maybe Peter would be outed. Just as on Mauna Kea, putting him at risk for an leak would be a dick move too, even though he'd leaked nothing more than that there would be an announcement about the killer.

When it hits mid-day in Hilo you know nothing's going to happen on the East Coast. Nobody schedules a press conference for dinnertime.

192

Early afternoon you hear your phone ringing. Becky checking in?

It's Peter. He says there won't be an announcement today, after all. He pauses. You say something like "Oh." You're getting ready to ask "When, then?" but before you can, he says "I can tell you the killer's not a member of the Harvard community, that he's nobody we know, and that he's dead."

You're speechless. A single sentence has shut you down. Hammered you. Shredded you. Everything's in that sentence, and it's nothing you ever expected to hear.

"Not a member of the Harvard community" excludes *everybody* you thought might have killed Jane. Every fucking one of them. Everything you thought you knew—blown up.

And dead? So there'll never be an explanation?

You can't remember what else you talked to him about. Probably nothing.

You remember standing there for a moment, phone in hand, feeling waves of emotion. Disappointment, shame, anger. And then, excitement. The thing you've waited half a century for has finally happened, but it isn't going the way you want. This can't be all there is! You want a name. You want to know what happened. More, more. You want more.

Then you flip into dismay: *All wrong, all wrong. All these years, wrong.*

Because you assume this must be DNA-related, you take no pleasure in having called it on Sunday, the DNA sweeping up an unknown killer. That was something anybody could have said.

193

You go find Ruth and tell her. She's glad, but also disappointed. She reminds you there's more to come. You know that, but right then it doesn't matter.

It's only been three or four minutes since Peter's call.

You call Becky.

That too seems strange. The times you've imagined calling her, you've always told her who the killer was, and that he was someone you both suspected.

All you can do is repeat what Peter told you: not Harvard, no one we know, dead.

Becky takes it differently than you did. Her voice is excited. She says she's relieved that whoever did it is dead. You don't ask her what that means. You're getting angry. *Fucker's dead*, you think, *no suffering for him*. You wanted him to *hurt*. You don't remember saying any of this to Becky, but when you ask her in 2020 that's how she describes it. You talk for a few minutes and then disconnect.

You realize that while Becky's invested in a *solution*, you've been invested in a *person*. Already it's hard letting go of Lee. All these years you've carried Lt. Joyce's "he could have been involved" as your fallback. Yes, other names have bubbled up and been attractive, but Lee's was the only name mentioned by a detective. Peter never revealed who he suspected, if anyone.

All wrong, all wrong, all wrong.

Sooner or later there'll be a name.

Sooner or later we'll know what happened.

## Boyd Calls

In the afternoon you stabilize. Every time you've thought about what a solution would *feel* like, it always involved vindication. *I knew it all along.* And now it doesn't, but hey—there *is* a solution. And uncertainty, but today's the point at which everything changed. July 25th, 2018. It needs marking. So you'll plant a tree for Jane.

There's just time to get to Garden Exchange, where you've been buying ʻōhiʻa trees and planting them along your front border. You planted one for Becky; you'll put Jane's near it. Their roots will intertwine. At Garden Exchange there are two large ones. One is perfect, beautifully shaped. The other has thick twisted branches, growing every which way. It's an easy choice.

You say to Ruth, "Jane needs a badass ʻōhiʻa." The two of you wrestle it in the 4Runner and take it up the hill.

You send Becky a picture. She replies, "Oh she's beautiful."

Then you wait.

On Mauna Kea, Peter said that Boyd would be told first, and then you. Maybe he told Boyd more than he told you?

On cue, an email from Boyd. Had you heard from Sgt. Sennott?

You email back that you have, and Boyd replies that he'll call you later with what he knows. It's 9 PM in California; dinnertime in Hilo.

You and Ruth eat dinner. It's a beautiful late afternoon in Hilo. The sun's streaming into the kitchen, where you always eat. It's only been four hours, and you're still processing what's happened.

Out of nowhere, a surge of emotion. You feel blood vessels dilating. Your heart lurches.

There's Ruth across the table. She's been at your side, an anchor, a defender. You love her more than you've ever loved anyone, and she knows it. A line from one of her poems comes into your head: *Nothing you can say is more than I can bear.*

"It's over," you say, your voice cracking.

"Yes," she says, and waits. Looks at you.

A surge. "I never gave up," you say, as the tears start. "I never gave up."

"Your gift to her."

You dry your eyes with your napkin. Reach down and pet the cat, who may have come for food, may have come to comfort you. You think, *I gave up last fall, though.*

You'll learn more when Boyd calls. You're impatient, but you don't think you should call him. You waited almost 50 years for this and you can wait a little longer.

It's early evening when Boyd calls. He wastes no time.

"Home invasion, possibly a stalker. Rape and murder."

A gut punch.

"Rape?"

"He raped her."

You don't remember what else you talked about.

You put down your phone and go to Ruth.

"Rape and murder by a stalker."

Ruth starts to cry. "Every woman's nightmare," she says, "Oh God. Poor Jane. Poor, poor Jane."

It's already 2 AM in Cambridge. Too late to call Becky. You email her that you'll call her around 5:30 AM.

Again you think, *All wrong, all wrong.*

The worst wrong is that you'd never tried to imagine what it was like for Jane. You'd always assumed that, after a quick strike in mid-argument, she lost consciousness and never came to. Like never coming out of an anesthetic.

Shibai, your own this time. All bullshit. You invented a convenient drama, too. Over quickly. Not conscious. You sanitized it.

Behind the shibai lurked what you hadn't allowed yourself to see: there must have been a time when she was experiencing *being attacked*, experiencing *being beaten*. And, you now know, experiencing *being raped*.

There must have been a time when she hoped he meant only to rape her. That afterward she'd be alive.

You walk around the house. Out onto the porch, where the sky's clear. Even though it's dark, you go down the steps, drag the hose out to Jane's ʻōhiʻa and give it some water, even though it doesn't need watering.

You go back in and sit at your computer for a while. You're unsettled, antsy. What to do now? Are there people you should email about this? Although Peter didn't swear you to secrecy explicitly, "this phone call never happened" is pretty damn close. You decide to honor it, so you don't email Todd, you don't email Alyssa. You imagine yourself emailing Jill. Two hours ago when you said *I never gave up*, you thought of her, she who did give up, she who wouldn't help and you thought *She hasn't earned it*.

You don't remember going to bed. You must have read for a time, as always. Cat on the bed. Ruth must have been by your side, as always. This was hard on her, too. Your house—it was her house, too—had been filled with Jane and Becky for more than a year. You don't think those two presences pushed anything out of the way, but they did make the place crowded. Ruth never complained.

In the night you woke and felt something leaving you, and knew it was about Jane. Perhaps what left was *Lee killed her*. You turned to Ruth, put your arms around her, and slept.

You're always up by 5, so at 5:30 you're fully awake and at the kitchen table drinking coffee. "Ready when you are," Becky texts. It hasn't been a week since "this call never happened."

Your only memory of the call is that you struggled to control yourself. You walked around the kitchen trying not to talk too loudly and wake Ruth or the neighbors. But you couldn't help raising your voice: "Becky the fucking sonofabitch raped her!"

That's the thing neither of you had known. Nobody knew it except the cops. You say, "How the hell did they keep that secret for 50 years?" Not *why*, because that was obvious.

You can't remember what else you talked about.

It's clear, now, why Peter never took DNA from Jill. The sample must have been semen. The murder weapon DNA focus: ashtray, handaxe—shibai. But it was your shibai, not his. He probably *was* just making conversation about the ashtray.

Did you lose it on the phone that morning? *Probably*, you think. Becky remembers you were angry at yourself for the narrative that masked the brutal reality of her death. You say to yourself *It's just how I dealt with it*, but that feels like a cop-out.

Then you begin thinking about how, in fiction, you haven't given Kate a voice beyond what Elliot hears. Is that the same thing? You say to yourself, *I don't know. Maybe. I can't think about Kate now*, and so you give it a rest.

It's light enough, so you grab your camera and tripod, go outside, and look for a shot. For the past 1,454 days you've made a shot in your house or yard, and posted it on a site called Hilo Daily Image. It's another kind of meditation practice for you: find a shot in a limited space, every morning. After you shoot and process and post it, you head out to the yard to see about prepping for Jane's 'ōhi'a.

The lava's close to the surface where you want to plant it, so it's going to be tricky. You can see there's a crevice, and you think maybe you can crack and pry out some of the lava, which is from a flow that came down from Mauna Loa more than 10,000 years ago. But there's no hurry. Jane's 'ōhi'a can stay in its pot for weeks, if it has to. You'll plant it when the press conference happens.

When you come back inside you say to Ruth, "We still don't know anything about the killer."

## A New Novel, and Boyd Calls Again

Three weeks pass. Becky's book project now needs a major revision. Because you and she don't share what she's written, you don't know where she was in the project when it blew up. You don't ask how she's going to handle it. You and Becky have been talking about her book cover, though. It's going to be based on the *This is who I am* shot that so strongly affected you both.

Becky's told you she doesn't know her publisher's budget for the cover. Out walking one day, you decide how you want to handle it. You tell her you're not going to allow a big New York publisher to have the image for nothing, but if they won't pay, you'll license it to her for a token sum, and she can license it to them. No matter what, you say, she'll get the cover you both want.

You're still waiting to hear about the press conference. Every time Peter gives you a tentative date it's cancelled.

"It's political," he emails at one point. You don't know what that means in practice because you know nothing about Massachusetts politics. Perhaps it's related to what he told you on Mauna Kea—that they don't like to release the name of a person who can't defend himself. It's

Fall, and you do know that the DA's in a close election, so maybe that's what's happening—they're working out how to maximize the benefit to her. You don't bother running that past Peter; you know it's something he would never talk about.

So you wait.

The 'ōhi'a stays in its pot.

You create a folder called Old Novel on your iMac and drag the many versions of the old Jane novel into it. It's hard to say goodbye. You're going to miss the Mesiamo-Elliot team. You're going to miss Lakabula and Kate. You're sorry you can't write Anna and her underground radical cell into it. You're not sorry to leave the killing and its intractable motive, though. You feel relief about that. Clean sheet, except for Kate, and you never did develop her much anyway.

Within a few days of Peter and Boyd's calls, the new novel begins coming to you. The fact that the killer was unknown to anybody is the key. You think about the times you've fantasized about avenging Jane by killing Lee, and from there a plot follows quickly: what if one of Kate's friends—no, her lover, another student you've named Max—has an unexpected chance to kill the man he thinks killed Kate—another graduate student, Desmond—and takes it? And it looks so much like an accident that no one questions it?

What if this happens a year or two after Kate's murder, and you set the main action in the present, so what Max did has receded almost as far into the past as Kate's murder has? What if Kate's case is cold until DNA reveals the true killer? What if one call from Massachusetts transforms Max from avenger to murderer—and Max is the only one who knows?

You like it, not least because of how shocking and difficult Max's transformation will be for him.

You know from one of the friends who'd been with you at Puʻu Lāʻau during the missile warning how easy going through the thin roof of a lava tube when off-trail on Mauna Loa can be. It had nearly happened to him; he caught himself on the lip and levered himself back out, using his rock-climbing skills. He told you his body would never have been found.

You decide to make Max a contract archaeologist who leaves Harvard without a degree and returns to Hilo, a failure—not because being a contract archaeologist is a failure, but because he never completed his degree. When he was young, in Hilo, great things were expected of him. Now he's back, working for hotels and developers.

When Desmond, who's been in Honolulu for a conference, comes to the Big Island, he asks Max to show him some sites. Max, who has hidden his suspicions from Desmond, takes him to a site high on Mauna Loa.

Two go up, one comes down. People who knew what search and rescue was like in the early 1970s told you that unless Max confessed, no one would suspect that it was anything but an unfortunate accident. People can disappear on Mauna Loa.

Why does Desmond kill Kate? You don't have to make that believable, because he didn't. You only need Max to convince himself of it, and for the police to make no move against Desmond, so that Max believes Desmond got away with murder.

You don't have to wrestle with the same problems you faced with your Eric character, or, in the real world, with Lee. You only need for Max to have a deep, burning anger towards Desmond, as you had towards Lee.

You start making notes and writing. It feels workable. Max differs strongly from Elliot, so you'll have the pleasure of creating a new character. Elliot never killed anybody, but Max will.

The eruption winds down. No more earthquakes. No more glow in the sky. It's taken hundreds of homes, reshaped a bay, and the bottom's dropped out of Kilauea Crater. It seems to be the end of an eruption that's lasted more than thirty years.

Then there's a hurricane warning.

Boyd calls.

"I have a name now," he says, and tells you a few things about the killer, an African-American man named Michael Sumpter. He may have killed women before Jane and he did kill after her. He raped other women.

The last thing Boyd tells you is about the troublesome ochre you thought the killer had thrown over her.

"It seems to have been hers, for painting. It was scattered when they fought," Boyd says.

You raise your voice. "Fought? She fought him?"

"Yes."

*Jane didn't go quietly.* You don't remember what else you talked about.

You repeat it to yourself. *She fought him. She fought him.*

You go tell Ruth. You hug.

In the morning, you call Becky.

"When Boyd said she fought with him, my heart lifted."

You clear your throat.

"Like, you know, 'fuck you, you son of a bitch' and they fight."

You cough again to cover your breaking voice.

"And she lost."

Becky's quiet. You're thinking about how the two of you have shared your sadnesses, your pain, your anger. Have shared dreams of a solution awash in—for you—vindication, even vengeance. And you haven't gotten that. You haven't really settled down from from what you learned three weeks ago. Peter and Boyd's calls gave you information, but that information hasn't led to closure.

And you're still unsettled and angry at yourself for having failed to put yourself in Jane's place because you'd developed your own shibai. Becky's right: you were protecting yourself, but that's hard to accept. Aren't you the guy who can imagine anything? Certainly in the last 49 years you could have, if you'd ever wanted to, gone beyond the simple physical sequences you'd given Peter and the others. First *he* did this, then *he* did that, then it was over.

But what did *Jane* do? Not only did you never try to inhabit her thoughts, you also made her passive—despite everything you knew about her. Everything you remembered about her.

You don't know how or why this happened. You can't remember ever saying to yourself *Don't go there.* You can't remember ever beginning to go there, and stopping yourself, either. Blank wall. Calling it a defense seems too simple to you, but it's clear you're not going to work it out quickly.

Never mind. Because you know Jane went down fighting, you're suffused with something like joy. And a calmness. Jane seems more real to you than she had, all those years when she was the character in your drama.

Your shibai.

After the call you go out to the ʻōhiʻa in its black plastic pot, sitting on the lava. You put your arms around it, pulling a delicate yellow blossom against your cheek.

"Goddam it, Jane," you whisper, "You fought the bastard."

# Planting the 'Ōhi'a

August-September, 2018. Radiation continues. You've learned how to present with your bladder at the right level.

In the parking lot at the Oncology Center, a pickup has a bumper sticker you like: "Do No Harm, Take No Shit." *Isn't that kind of Buddhist?* you wonder.

An August hurricane that hits as a tropical storm drops record amounts of rain on your side of the island. You spend time photographing the rivers and falls. Luckily, you've bought a new raincover for your camera, so you don't care how hard it's raining. You don't bother covering yourself up. As the Nagovisi used to say, "Am I sugar, that rain melts me?"

Becky researches the Chicago polygraph guy who had the God question. She texts you that he was the actor Woody Harrelson's uncle, and that Woody's father was a criminal. You Google him and learn that he was an armed robber and hitman who died in prison, and bragged about killing JFK.

You think *Can this get any weirder?*

You text Peter, who replies that he'd heard that Woody's father was "a jailbird" and now "you got the proof" for "another chapter for your book." Your book? Becky's! But it's all good. You no longer hold back anything from him.

You submit three Mauna Kea photographs to an island-wide exhibition. The jurors take them all. It's been 14 years since you've had a print hanging in an exhibition, and now you have three. The framer at the place you take the prints turns out to be a friend of your Buffalo framer. You like that.

Despite the radiation and another testosterone-blocking shot, you set about digging out large clumps of bamboo you planted eight years ago. They grew much faster and spread more widely than they were supposed to. Bamboo is exceedingly difficult to dig out, and you're weak. You can only work hard for five or ten minutes before needing to rest. At one point you're swinging your pickaxe, lose your balance, and pitch over into the hole. No damage, but your first thought is *I hope nobody saw that.* Then you call Ruth to come take a picture of you *in extremis.*

You take the 4Runner up to 11,000' on Mauna Loa and shoot across the Saddle to Mauna Kea's summit, to get some pictures of the observatories. A friend—the Director of the Canada-France-Hawaiʻi telescope—needs them for a website. It's a clear morning, not much atmospheric distortion, and the pictures are excellent.

The observatories are more than 20 miles away, and when you send them to the Director he's astonished to see the snowplow guides on the road shoulders. You love hearing that from a guy whose telescope sees across the universe. Your Nikon D850 didn't seem quite the equal of his optics, but you knew, as he knew, that you'd delivered him what he needed because you had the right tool for the job, and knew how to use it.

Not everything's easy. You and some of your Mauna Kea people are invited back to Honolulu to meet with the Governor, a few state department heads, and the President of the University. It's your second trip over. They're interested in what you've done—that's the plural you. You're feeling effects from the radiation, and aren't sure you should go. The other people in your group prevail, so you catch a flight over.

The meeting goes well, but at one point you're asked to speak about something and, not far into it, you lose control of your topic. You don't exactly trail off, but it's clear you're floundering. Fortunately, one of your group picks it up and makes your points. Nobody looks hard at you or seems unhappy, but the next day you write your colleagues an email apologizing for having let them down.

You'd gotten used to having your body not deliver what you asked, but to have your mind fail you, when in the company of important people who wanted to hear what you had to say? That felt awful.

In early September another hurricane seemed to be headed to the Big Island, so you decide to plant Jane's ʻōhiʻa rather than waiting for the DA's announcement. It's been sitting in the front yard, in its pot. Neighbors walking on the street have asked about it. They've watched you plant—what is it now, sixteen?—ʻōhiʻa along the front border. Everybody approves, because ʻōhiʻa, the foundational tree of Hawaiʻi forests, is under siege from an invasive fungus that looks as though it might kill half of them. So planting ʻōhiʻa is almost a civic duty.

One day you're asked again and you decide to explain. "A friend of mine was murdered almost 50 years ago," you say, "in Massachusetts, and they're supposed to announce that the crime's been solved, and when they do I'm going to plant this ʻōhiʻa as a memorial to her."

The walkers are surprised. "Really? Fifty years? They caught the guy?" And you have to say, "Yes, but he's dead," and then you tell them that when they see the ʻōhiʻa planted, they'll know it's been wrapped up.

There hasn't been any announcement and you're planting it anyway. You'll have to explain. You've already done all the hard work of cracking open the lava flow, horsing a few large chunks of lava out of the way, digging and filling the hole with compost and volcanic cinders.

You tell Becky that you'll make a video. Ruth asks if you want her to video you. After a moment, you say "No," that you'll mount your phone on a tripod and just let it run. You tell her you want to be alone, even though that seems weird, considering that you're making a video to send around, and you're doing it in the front yard.

It's not that you're confused; you're just wanting to ease into what you know will be an *ad hoc* ritual. You have no plan beyond the obvious: open up the hole, put the tree in it. Somewhere in that sequence the right things will happen, but you don't want to be self-conscious about it, even with Ruth.

You decide not to change out of the purple Piʻihonua Neighborhood Association t-shirt you have on. It's not about what you're wearing. Everything you need is nearby—tools, black cinders, compost. You get to work, talking to the camera from time to time. You feel emotion but you're also wishing that you were planting it on the day of the announcement.

When it's finished, you don't feel a sense of completion beyond the obvious. Nothing you said caught in your throat. Nothing produced an upwelling of emotion.

You take the rig inside to your room, sit at your desk, bring up the picture of Jane that's going to be on Becky's cover on your display, and talk to the camera. You look like a guy who's just done some physical labor. There are sweat stains on your shirt.

You talk about the tree as symbolizing not only Jane's death, but a kind of rebirth. This wasn't scripted; it came to you while you were outside. One of the things you didn't expect, you say, was feeling the need to take off your gloves so as to have nothing between your hands and the cinder as you smoothed it around the trunk.

You edit the video, moving the audio around. You add some footage of you when you were wrestling large chunks of lava away from the hole. You add still pictures of Jane, including *This is who I am.* You add a soundtrack, that Bach organ toccata she played for you that has always embodied her. Over the years it's become your trigger. It's a mighty piece, with a strong descending pedal figure that, each time it repeats, goes lower.

When you play through the final cut, listening on your headphones, cranking up the volume so that Bach overpowers everything, what you thought would happen outside happens at your desk. Tears. You think it's because the video encapsulates what you now know about Jane's death, the ʻōhiʻa, the still images, and the music. You realize that you've put it all together for the first time.

Yes, outside you were fully aware, you were in the moment, but it wasn't until you took what you'd captured, creatively modified it, and then played it for yourself that some barrier broke in you. You needed to see what you made of what you'd done.

Tell me my own story.

You wrapped your arms around yourself and spun in your chair, in and out of the light from your window. Your own drama. Yes, the shibai *you* created. The larger drama's been playing for half a century but just now you brought it all together and you realize is that the killer's nowhere in your thinking. You have his name, you know what he did, but you know nothing else about him and you don't need to. Don't want to.

You haven't replaced Lee with him. You don't even hate him. He's nothing more than the anonymous agent of Jane's death, no different to you than an out-of-control car or a fire or fatal illness. You're not going to make the mistake of granting him a leading role as you'd granted Lee one.

It comes to you that for all these years you've allowed the villain's part to grow larger than Jane's. To grow at her expense. To crowd her out. In fixating on the villain you were annulling Jane. Now, Jane's free to be herself, to take up her own role in the great shibai that somehow, without intent, you've managed to capture by creating a video: the still images as Jane-who-was, the Bach as Jane-who-has-endured, the ʻōhiʻa as Jane-reborn.

You send the video to Becky, without whom Jane would not have been reborn, and to Boyd.

Months later it occurs to you that the emotional fragility— the sobbing, the tears—that came upon you in the late summer and fall might have been connected with your hormone imbalance, and you remember a talk you had with the urologist during which you joked "Will I burst into tears in Safeway?" and he replied "Only if they don't have the cream cheese you're looking for."

You were joking because you were—you had to admit it to yourself later—frightened. That was the first day he'd been explicit: *yes you have cancer.* In other words that was the first day it became real to you and so—what else—you joked about it.

It had been one thing to take pictures of your balls on your earlier trip to Honolulu, but quite another to sit there with Ruth and listen to an explicit treatment plan.

You realize you'd been imagining the possible emotional changes as *pervasive*, coloring your entire attitude toward the world, rather than something lying dormant until triggered.

You have your last blast of radiation in mid-September. The predicted fatigue finally arrived, and you're wiped out for a day or two. After that, you're still weak, but you get to work on the front border. The new ʻōhiʻa are in place, eight feet apart, but between them there's nothing. So you plant flowers, pineapples, pikake, taro, and whatever else you can find at the nurseries around town. You move some honeysuckle from where your mother planted it when you were a boy. It's got to be 65 or 70 years old.

This takes you two weeks and it's a test. Will you get stronger each day? You do.

Two weeks later, you're again texting with Peter. You ask about the announcement, and he says "Politics. It's coming." This time, he doesn't give you any numbers.

# The 'Ōhi'a Redux

IN EARLY NOVEMBER, you and Peter are texting about football. You texted about the Patriots and Bills, hoping that the Patriots wouldn't humiliate the Bills. It's really only an excuse to contact him. At the end of the exchange you write, "I don't suppose there's any news, is there?" but he doesn't respond.

You've already made plans to visit your son and his family in Brooklyn. You and Ruth have reservations to fly out of Hilo on the 19th. Becky says she'll come down from Cambridge for a day or two. You know you won't be talking about her book, but you're looking forward to spending some time with her.

Then, on the 16th, Becky calls with the news she got before you did. There's going to be a press conference on the 20th.

"All right!" you say, and the two of you talk about whether you should head for Boston after you get to Brooklyn. You don't think it's practical. You repeat how good this is, and that even though Ruth's getting into the shower, you're going to go tell her. "And the cat," you say. You're almost giddy. It's finally happened. It's going public.

Later in the day you write Becky that you're "having complex emotions…enormous gratitude towards you and

Todd and Michael and Alyssa for push push pushing and making this happen. And then the whole mixture of feelings about having been wrong for so long, and having given up on Peter."

Time's short. The ritual that never quite evolved? The video that affected you so strongly weeks ago doesn't feel like one, although in freeing Jane it's also freed you. And you continue to have no interest in the killer. He's nothing to you.

Long ago you thought about putting a maile lei—a sweet-smelling green-leafed vine lei—on the tree when the killer was publicly named. Maile is often used at funerals; both your mother's and your father's ash containers were draped with maile. But it's in short supply just now, and people are asking that it not be harvested for leis without good reason.

You go to the store where it's usually in the lei cooler, but they have nothing. You go on Facebook and ask your Hilo friends for advice. One of them suggests the lei seller at the Hilo airport, and this surprises you because although you're aware that there's one in the terminal, you've never paid attention to it.

When you were young, the airport was the main source of leis. You remember seeing a dozen or more small stands along the road, each draped with leis in different flowers, different styles. But that's been gone for years, and now there's only one, and you have to go into paid parking to get to it.

They're just closing. They don't have any, but the guy says they can make them over the weekend and have them for you Monday. He runs your card and tells you there's no need for the parking lot. Just text when you're outside and we'll bring them out. Not exactly the same as when your mother would pull over by the old lei stands, and you'd get out with some bills and give her order to the lei maker.

Monday, after you get the leis, you start feeling that you haven't completed the ritual, even though you don't know what it should be. You thought again about that old story "Burials," which had been on your mind lately precisely because the two characters in it created their own ritual —"the thing we were about to do, but did not know how to do, nor know what its meaning would be when we did do it."

You go back to thinking about the video. Is there another way to bring it all together? Yes. Put part of her, part of you, part of Becky in the ground with her. Once you have the idea, the rest is easy.

You find a screw-top plastic container, ex-Talenti gelato. *She'd like that,* you think.

You print out the last page of the Bach score, her death certificate, and two portraits of her that you love.

You add a piece of the maile lei you'll put around the tree.

You add a picture of you and Becky, friend of your heart and companion on this journey, and, finally, a strand of the red shell valuables called *wiasi* from Nagovisi, given to you by the woman you call Siuwako. Passing it to Jane will, you feel sure, please Siuwako.

You wrap the container with duct tape, get the video rig, and head outside. Alone. This time, you're wearing your best aloha shirt.

At the 'ōhi'a you take Jane's maile from your neck, and say "Jane, this is for you." You go to your knees, encircle the trunk with it, and, hands on thighs, remain still for a moment. Then you sigh. When you rise, dirt on your knees, you say to the camera, "That's the end of something."

You put the other lei around Becky's ʻōhiʻa, and then you bury the capsule.

You say, "We go on from here," and then you say, voice cracking, "Bye, Jane," and then you say again, "Bye."

# THE REVEAL

IN THE HONOLULU AIRPORT you decide it's time to tell Jill, so you forward her the press release Becky forwarded to you. You can't resist telling her that you learned about this back in July. She asks the obvious question, "Who is it?" and you reply, "Nobody we knew. And he's dead. An evil man who killed before Jane and probably afterward. He died in prison in 2001." You give her his name.

"Poor Jane. Such a waste," she responds.

You write, "Here's one thing that made me feel better. She fought him. She didn't go quietly," to which Jill replies "Yes, that would be Jane." After that, unsurprisingly, her emails shift to schooling you about Cambridge's Black population, and asserting herself as an authority on something she'd known about for perhaps twenty minutes. That she was writing to someone who'd been immersed in the case for well over a year, and who'd been in regular contact with the MSP must have seemed unimportant to her.

*Yes*, you think, *That would be Jill.* But it annoys you.

Before getting on the plane you email Peter: "You rock, my friend. You rock! I thank you from the bottom of my heart," to which he replies, "People like you make this work. Stay in Hawaii, it's cold here."

And to Todd, "At last! And of course you played in a big part in making this happen. I'm very grateful to you."

When you finally arrive at your son's place your body time is lagging six hours, and you're coming off of eleven hours in an economy seat, but you're ready. You settle in with your laptop to watch the press conference, but first there are emails from Todd, who needs to interview you, and from from Alyssa—luckily—with a better link than the one you've been trying to use.

You're excited to watch the press conference, but the excitement is because it's finally happening, not because of anything the DA reveals. Apart from some new information about the killer—which doesn't interest you—there's nothing you haven't known about. Still, it's pleasant to see Peter standing there in a suit. You keep looking for Becky, but the camera on the stream you're looking at never drifted over to the audience.

Later in the day, more emails with Todd, and a phone interview. The *Globe*'s website posts a picture of Jane that you took, but credits it to the DA's office. You're sure it's a scan of a picture you gave the Cambridge detective who went with you to your darkroom, so you ask Todd if the attribution could be changed. He replies that the photo editors are reluctant to do that with no evidence other than your assertion, which makes sense to you. Of course they are.

But you have some of the Jane negative scans on your laptop, so you email Todd an image of one strip that, although it doesn't include the frame in question, shows Jane in a similar pose with an identical background. That's good enough for the photo editors, and in the next edition and the website, you're credited. And Todd posts some other pictures of Jane you sent him.

You're feeling good about this. Back in 1969, the newspaper pictures of Jane were horrible yearbook images. In the ones you've sent Todd, she's the beautiful young woman you remember.

Peter calls, and you thank him again. You ask if he can say how many DNA samples he took, and he says "six or seven." You know better than to ask who they were, but you wish you could, because your list of possibles was never more than three long. Later, he texts you, "Thank you for everything you did. You really made this case memorable to a late comer in the scene." That pleases you, even though you know you didn't play a major role. You gave him a lot of background information, and maybe cleared up some uncertainties. But as for nailing the killer—you had nothing to do with that.

You post about the case on Facebook, where you haven't mentioned it previously. You post the same message on websleuths. You started with the chronology, talked about Becky, talked about Peter's visit to Hilo to get your DNA, and you talked about how you came to believe it was only shibai. Then you got to what you wanted to say publicly:

> For almost half a century I suspected that certain man killed my friend, but now I know he was innocent. I owe him an apology that I can't give to him because he is no longer alive. Having a strongly-held belief like that turned upside down is humbling.
>
> For almost half a century I believed that Jane had somehow gotten herself into a situation that unexpectedly and lethally turned bad. Mainly this was because most of us only looked for suspects within our own crowd, the anthropologists and

archaeologists, and none of us seemed to be violent killers. So we thought Jane must have died because something unexpectedly escalated into lethal violence.

For all those years, though, I never could come up with a possible situation that didn't seem strained or flawed.

I don't think that any of us who knew Jane ever thought that her death was a random act of violence. I know I didn't. But it was, and so that's another thing I have to process. Don't cling to a hypothesis that doesn't seem quite right just because it's the only one you can think of. But that's what I did and it's a sobering thought.

People talk about closure, and I guess that's what I have now. I know how Jane Britton died which means I now know something I deeply wanted to know for half a century. And, to tell the truth, I always wondered whether I was still considered a suspect, particularly when Sgt. Sennott came to collect DNA from me. Over the years, I've wondered how many people out there thought I might have been the killer; now, if they're paying attention to the news, they know I'm not.

Jane's story needs to be told—and not just the story of the crime, although that's the nexus. The Anthropology Department, all of us, the Cambridge community and how it was in the late sixties and the ways that Jane's story has endured and has been passed from student to student all these years. And more subtly, the ways Jane and her story have influenced our lives over the years—

well, I should only speak for myself. I don't think
two months have ever gone by that I didn't think
of her. And the ways those of us who never forgot
her, who, like me, never completely abandoned
hope that the case could be solved, helped keep
her memory alive.

A few more emails, some texts, and you collapse.

Two days later you carefully compose an email to Jill and
Andrea. You're hoping to convince them to talk to Becky;
both have refused to be interviewed. It's as non-aggressive
and non-judgmental as you can make it.

I'm writing because I'm hoping you'll rethink your
decision not to talk to Becky Cooper about the
case. *We would not know what we know now*—there
would have been no resolution—without Becky,
Alyssa Bertetto, Todd Wallack and Michael
Widmer.

You go on to summarize Becky's visit. You write,

Nothing that's happened since then has made
me doubt my decision to cooperate with her...the
book is really about the Anthropology Department
and Cambridge. Yes, it's about a horrible murder.
But Becky's putting it all in context and carrying
the story forward to the present. I can't count
the number of times I said to Becky, "I can't
remember, but I'm sure Jill can," or "Jill would
know about that." The book will be a better book
if your story's part of it.

You close with "If you're grateful to Becky for forcing
this to a resolution, why not think about helping her out

221

in return? And seeing to it that as much of Jane's story as can be told, will be told?"

It doesn't work. Jill replies the same day—a rant that doesn't address what you wrote. "I did not know that Jane had been raped until these new stories came out. How in the hell could the cops not see a violent misogynist had been responsible? I had envisioned the bludgeoning as an argument which got out of control."

You read on, shaking your head. Not only is she not filling in any blanks, her memory's faulty. She believes that she, not you, called in the ochre, and to the MSP rather than the Cambridge cops.

She agrees that "pressures from journalists must have affected the decision to retest DNA," but that's as far as she'll go. Her penultimate sentence is "Jane is still dead and now I know she had a frightening experience that is every woman's worst nightmare before she died." Her final sentence is an obscenity directed at "the cops."

You were hoping to convince her to help Becky—help Jane, really—but she doesn't respond directly to that request. *She could have just said no*, you think. Instead, you got the usual lecture that she knew more than you did (or had thought more carefully about it), and a flood of unwarranted assertions, *non sequiturs*, complaints, and the revisiting of old grievances.

*Pretty much her way*, you think.

But in the mess there was something of value: "we were …identified to the grand jury as the #1 perps." There it is: confirmation of what Paul and Sally had told you back then and you'd believed all those years.

You forward the email to Becky and try to forget about it. Andrea never replies.

Over the next few days you explore the coverage. *The New York Times* has thin coverage; you write them an email reminding them that they even sent a reporter to Cambridge to interview you in 1969. *The Washington Post* has excellent coverage and, unlike the *Globe*'s in 2017, you jump into the comments section under your usual handle, but you identify yourself. It's satisfying. Todd's *Globe* articles are great, but you leave the comment sections alone.

A couple of days after the press conference you're helping your son put up siding on an entryway. You're using the compressor and nail guns you bought for him, and suddenly you remember the compressor link you accidentally texted Peter the year before, which led to his telling you that you'd been cleared. You can't let that pass by, so you take some pictures of the compressor, hoses, power miter and extension cords and text them to him. You think about referring to "you're cleared," but you don't. Either he remembers it or he doesn't. It's fine either way.

Back home, the oncologist tells you that you're clean. You'll need to keep monitoring things, but there's no sign of cancer. After telling Ruth and Becky and your son, you text Peter, who replies, "Jane is watching over you."

Then you turn to Mary and her boyfriend. It's time to use that audio clip. Not caring whether they're still together or not, you write them a joint email in which you lay out what had happened, tell them "Listen to the recording I've attached before even thinking about denying what you did," and finish up with "I expect you both felt pretty cute about this at the time. You must have had no idea how far out of your depths you were, fucking around with the Massachusetts State Police. And with me. Shame on both of you," which feels pretty good.

You don't think you'd get an answer, but you do. The boyfriend writes, "here is much to be thankful for: including the killer of Jane Britton has finally been identified and that he is not you...This must be a great relief for you after all these years," which makes you laugh so hard you begin coughing.

What's with these people who can't own what they've done? Cowards.

## LEAVING IT ALL BEHIND

YOU CONTINUE TO WORK on the novel, which is coming along nicely. It's getting more complex. You're undecided about how Max will kill Desmond. Shall it be overt (he topples Desmond into a lava tube and leaves him)? Shall he lead him into an area of what's called "shelly pahoehoe," a kind of lava that covers cavities only one or two feet deep that looks strong but will break under one's weight? When that happens, one person tells you, there's going to be a broken bone, or at least a serious sprain. If this happens at high elevation in the afternoon fog, then that person's going to be on the mountain overnight, and exposure's likely to kill him if he's not prepared. Max can then blame Desmond for his own death.

Although you almost always walk alone, you occasionally walk with a neighbor who was an ER doctor. You tell him about the shelly pahoehoe plan and he says that it's worse than what you heard. He's seen people who cut themselves on the sharp edge of a break, opened up an artery, and bled to death. You like this, because Max can trick Desmond the same way, but doesn't have to depend on exposure. Desmond bleeds out.

The issue's important because when Max finally learns that Desmond wasn't the killer, the way he deals with it is going to depend on how he sees his culpability. Straight out homicide? Negligent homicide? Reckless endangerment? At least the options are becoming clear to you.

Then it's time to head for New Mexico where, surprisingly for you (but not Ruth, an ex-English professor) you've been named Jack Williamson Visiting Professors of English at Eastern New Mexico University, in Portales, the same town that named you and Ruth Visiting Artists back in 2013. It's very satisfying. The students are good, the faculty great, you give several public readings, the food is fabulous and you get to spend time on a ranch.

It's flat, though. Very flat. The Portales joke is that if your horse runs away, you can see him for three days.

Portales and its vibrant arts scene makes you think about how it is in Hilo. Visual arts are excellent. Music is good. Hilo's literary scene? There isn't one. Even Portales and ENMU, way out in the desert, have a more active literary community—and, importantly, it's one that welcomes you and Ruth in a way that the Hilo scene never did.

You've both read at the Hilo Public Library and at Hilo's only bookstore, but you couldn't crack the University scene. This was a surprise to you, considering that you're a Hilo boy who even attended the university for a year while in high school. But the overtures you made were rejected; Ruth also had no success. Honolulu has an active scene, but being a part of it would mean flying there every time there was an event.

As much as you love Hilo and the Big Island, you both begin to wonder if moving back to Hilo was a wise choice.

You begin to feel each other out. Is this the best place for us right now? Shouldn't we try to be closer to places like New York, Boston, and Buffalo, where we were both part of the scene?

You meant to stay in Hilo until you die, but now you're wavering.

Becky continues to work on her book, although you don't talk as much as you did. You don't have new material to offer her, so there's no way for you to be helpful, except to send her parcels of Big Island goodies.

You decide that Lt. Chong, the helpful Hilo detective, deserves to know that Peter cracked the case, so you email him, and he replies: "From what I read in the article, it looks like that you've started mending things with yourself. May you find continued comfort in days to come." *That's Hilo,* you say to yourself, *we care about each other.*

You train for 76k and take your shot even though you're not quite ready. As always, you text Becky from 25.5k. The last 2k are rough. You're tired and unsteady on your feet. When you hit 76k and stop your watch, you topple over into the soft vines off the shoulder. It's your balance that went wrong, not your consciousness, so you're not worried. You lie there for a moment, pulling out your phone so you can take a picture of your watch. You'll get up after that.

Suddenly three women with concerned faces are looking down at you. They were driving by in different cars and saw you fall. They thought you might be having a heart attack. You tell them you're fine but they're not entirely convinced. One, a nurse, wants to check your pulse. You show her your watch—110, low enough to satisfy her. They start to help you up, and you almost refuse their help before you realize that's nuts. Let them help you!

Ruth has parked where she can't see any of this, so one of them goes over to get her. It's quite the little gathering. Three cars, four women, and one old guy in a green shirt and white cap who's just walked 47 miles. Hugs and photographs and Ruth takes you back to Hilo. Another year down.

Not long after that, a group of Native Hawaiians protesting a planned observatory on Mauna Kea block the road up the mountain and settle in. You understand their historic grievances and you know they're trying to put together a political movement, and that it's all about Hawaiian Sovereignty, but you don't think holding the observatories and the mountain hostage is the right path.

There's no way to get up the mountain or, if you're coming from its other side, to get down. This means you can't visit your parents' ashes. You can't go on your favorite tracks. If this were only a matter of inconvenience, it wouldn't bother you. But it's much more than that.

What's killing you this August is that the protestors are not interested the mountain beyond the small part of the summit where they don't want the observatory to be built. They don't care about the rest of the mountain. They don't care about the "soft voices" you and the Hui worked so hard to present. The protestors aren't representative of the thousands of people who love and use the mountain.

It kills you that so much of what they say are lies, and, worse, many of the people you know in Hilo believe those lies. Well-meaning people who don't know the mountain swallow them whole. You broke with friends, to whom you had suddenly been transformed into an outsider, even though you'd been born on the island, and they hadn't, even though you knew Mauna Kea and they didn't. Even though you knew the science and history, and they didn't.

One head-shaking example was the assertion that should there be an accidental spill of something at the summit, Hilo's water supply—miles away, with solid rock in between—would pollute Hilo's water supply.

Then there's the terror about the 250 ml (about 8 ounces) of mercury that was spilled up there years ago. Observatory laser guide-star beams are said to be military anti-satellite weapons. The observatories are huge money-making entities controlled by Bill Gates. The new one will be nuclear-powered. One is owned by Communist China. The conspiracy theories and lies go unchallenged by the media.

*Trump world on the Big Island,* you think, not because of politics, but because of the unending stream of alternative facts and anti-science screeds swallowed whole by the gullible.

When you went down to the police station you knew you'd be treated as *one of us* once you demonstrated that you were. Now, it doesn't matter. Child of the land or not, you're treated as an outsider, because to be an insider you have to support the protests. And you won't. Can't.

The County authorities prove themselves inept, or corrupt. They knew—everyone knew—the exact day that the protestors would make their move. Was anything done in preparation for that? No. Mayberry RFD. The protestors were masters of social media; the authorities belonged to the dial-up age. When the local paper called on experts to debunk the nonsense, it was too late. It had taken root.

If you were 50 years old, you tell your friends, or even 60, you'd stay, do what you could, and see it through. But you're closer to 80 than any other round-number age, and you can't spare the years.

You find yourself getting angry. What began as a small demonstration grew into a settlement of hundreds of shelters and semi-permanent structures. No one—not the County, not the State—could figure out what to do about it. It was completely out of hand.

You're invited to a secret meeting in Kona. When you arrive, guys with curly wires running from ear to aloha shirt greet you and check you in, so you know important people must be upstairs. When you enter the room, the Governor gets up and comes over to shake your hand, as does the President of the University. They remember you from the Honolulu meeting. Important state officials are there. The County Executive's there. Astronomers. Non-protesting Native Hawaiians, some prominent; they talk about harassment in their own communities.

You leave the meeting in gloom. No one seems to know what to do, what might work. Mass arrests are not an option. All you had to offer were some PR tactics that might have switched the conversation (which was hardly a *conversation*) away from the observatories and to the mountain as a whole, and from the protestors to the soft voices the Hui had heard and that you'd tried to amplify.

You post an article on a Honolulu news site, giving examples of what the soft voices had said, and asking that they be heard. In return you're attacked on Facebook, including by people you'd gone to Hilo High with.

As time goes on nothing changes and it seems to you nothing will. It's obvious that even if the protestors withdraw, they can regroup and shut down the mountain any time they want to. You—and everybody else who loves the mountain and needs to be on it—will be at their mercy.

You don't want to live in a place like that. Can't.

You feel as though your novel may be your last chance to make a little noise. Without a literary community of substance, working alone, you have no chance at all. If you find one somewhere else and can't work your way in, well, that's on you. But you want to try. Ruth feels the same way.

And your grandchildren live in Brooklyn. It's not hard to get to Ruth's grandchildren, in Los Angeles. And they're mostly grown, so a grandparental presence isn't so important. But the Brooklyn grandchildren are very young, and you realize that seeing them once a year for a few days is not the way to help raise them, and that you will never be a part of their growing up unless you're closer.

One afternoon in late August you and Ruth are standing in the front hall and you say, "It's time." She knows exactly what you mean. She's been thinking the same thing. You look at each other and almost with one voice you both say "Ithaca!" You know Ithaca from when you lived in Buffalo. It's close to New York, Boston, Buffalo. It's perfect.

You write to Becky, "it has a great combination of a world-class university (and a good liberal arts college) in a small town, with countryside nearby. To me, that's unbeatable."

Of course you waver a few times. This is, after all, your home town and the house you grew up in. Jane's tree's there, as is Becky's, and there are trees for the grandchildren, your daughter-in-law Leah's mother, and several friends. You'll miss them, but they don't need you to thrive.

One of the times you waver, Ruth says "I'm never leaving you, so if you stay, I stay."

In October you and Ruth fly to Ithaca and buy a solar-powered geothermally-heated house on a ridge surrounded by over a hundred thirty acres of woods, not far outside Ithaca. Done.

The Hilo house is set to go on the market in February 2020. Before that, you've got to paint it. Well, you've painted it before, and on the mainland you've painted other houses. Extension ladders hold no terrors for you but, it's true, the 24' fiberglass one is getting hard for you to handle. Even so, the painting goes quickly. *I can still do this*, you say to yourself more than once, high on a ladder, stretching out.

Some big invasive multi-trunked cinnamon trees need cutting down because they're tangling the power and signal lines from the pole, but that's no problem. First you prune them so they won't take the wires with them, then you fell them. You can drop a tree where you want it, with chainsaw or ax, because the Nagovisi taught you. Ruth helps.

'Ōhi'a the cat walks along the lanai railing, yowling. She doesn't like seeing the two of you down there amidst crashing branches and thumping trunks. Then you pull the large stumps, which is much harder than felling the trees.

You get fifteen tons of gravel so you can fill in a lava tube you've never worried much about. A potential buyer might not be at ease with the tube, which runs through the neighborhood and, in truth, cesspools overflow into it during heavy rain. Fifteen tons is a lot of wheelbarrow loads, but you get it done.

Everything you do now is directed towards being in Ithaca in late spring.

# NARNIA

YOUR HILO HOUSE is only a few hundred yards from the edge of the Wailuku River, where you and your neighborhood friends played as boys. The Wailuku could be dangerous—flash flooding was common—but the boys were careful. Your mother had rules: you couldn't go to the river if it could be heard from the house, and you couldn't go if Mauna Kea (where the upper branches of the river were) wasn't clear. You explored and played up river about a mile, but no farther.

When you moved back to Hilo you began hearing about a place upstream nicknamed Narnia. As a name for part of the Wailuku, that amused you. But then you began to notice that people were drowning there. Most years, the Wailuku takes two or three people; usually they are tourists who don't understand how dangerous it is.

One rainy day when you could hear the river from far away, you were returning from a walk and saw the orange search and rescue chopper over the Wailuku. The rescue folks had a truck and a canopy set up in the parking lot at Boiling Pots. The canopy always meant that somebody was waiting for a lost one to be found.

You walked home, cut anthuriums, sweet-scented cinnamon flowers and clove leaves, fragrant pikake, some honeysuckle, Kula gardenias, and walked back up to the mother waiting at the river while a helicopter searched for her daughter. When you gave them to her she cried, waiting, waiting near the river that took her child, whose body wasn't found for more than a month and never would have been found except that someone saw it going over a waterfall far downstream.

When you'd made up your mind to leave Hilo, you started walking to Narnia, which turned out to be a wonderful place—the confluence of the Wailuku and another large stream, creating four or five waterfalls, one of them very tall and set back among the 'ōhi'a so that all you could see was the river rushing over the top, falling fugitive behind the trees. When you came off the trail to the edge you gasped. This was not the Wailuku you knew. You were captivated. You don't like to call things *magical* but that's what it was.

You took pictures, sending them down the hill to Ruth and across the ocean to Becky. No one else was there then. People who went to Narnia to swim or hang out did so later in the day. You were usually there in the early morning.

Tanks, pipes, and purifying equipment for Hilo's water supply were up there. Access was blocked by a locked gate, but that was for vehicles. Walking around the gate was fine.

You began to explore. An early find was old water infrastructure, fallen into disrepair. Stone, concrete, metal, wood. Broken spillways. Wheels that no longer turned valves. You climbed up into them, took pictures. In another place, old pump houses covered with graffiti.

A couch had been stuffed into one of them. *Needles*, you thought, *don't sit down*. Higher up, there was none of that.

Before long the area captured you and you no longer cared about your workouts. You wanted to learn this new place so close to home, found only as you were readying yourself to leave.

One day you found a road that ran uphill for more than a mile between two large water tanks and was completely straight, and paved. It ran through what you could tell was old ranchland, now being taken over by forests. You saw wild pigs, so you made a lot of noise and made sure you always had a climbable tree in sight. You returned to that road regularly because by then you had started talking into your phone about your novel. On the road between Tank Two and Tank Three you didn't have to watch your footing and only once did you see another person.

You were still getting into Max's head, developing him. One day, because the novel's structure revolved around a long-term memoir-writing workshop at a senior center, you were thinking about the tsunami memoir Max would write, and you were thinking about Max and death, Max and murder. And when you thought about death you usually thought about Jane as well, but you never thought about her killer.

One day when you'd climbed to the top of the road and headed back down, you took out your phone. It was a beautiful morning. You could see down to Hilo and the ocean. You started in dictation mode: "OK. After Max escapes from the bridge and runs back to where the Rescue Squad is assembling…."

But soon, something happened that every fiction writer knows: Max took over and you began speaking

Max. And you didn't stop speaking Max for nearly half
an hour while walking slowly down the road. Max wanted
to talk about something you'd experienced—finding the
dead body—but he had his own story.

So we got to the hospital and how were three
teenage boys supposed to know where the morgue
was, but we figured, well, it doesn't matter.

We made the driver go to the emergency
room. There was a sign, we said "around there,
around there," giving directions. I got out of the
sampan and went to the emergency room. The
first person I saw had scrubs. I don't even know
what we called them then. I didn't know the word
scrubs. I said, "We have a dead person. What
should we do?" And he said, "Oh, I'll have the
morgue people come out. Where are you?"

I said, "We're in a sampan bus."

So I went back and I said, "Well, they're going
to send some people from the morgue so we might
as well take her out." I felt strongly, *we* have to
take her out. We brought her here, we found her,
we brought her here. It was like in a way that I
couldn't have talked about then, she was ours.

She was ours. We didn't save her from dying,
but we felt possessive. So we took her out and we
put her down on the driveway and we waited.

And in a short time two orderlies came with
a stretcher and they knew what they were doing.
They put the stretcher down next to her. This
couldn't have been the first body that they'd seen
that night. And they were older men.

They looked at us, and we looked at them, this was all in a moment. And then they made a move to pick her up, but we bent down and picked her up and put her on the stretcher. And then they picked up the stretcher, but we didn't want to leave her. We didn't know what the story was, but we knew it wasn't over.

So we walked with them, and the two orderlies on the ends of the stretcher, to the morgue and they opened up a door. They said, "You can't come in here." And one of them said to us, the one on the back, he turned to us and he said, "Boys, say goodbye now, say goodbye."

Then we said "Goodbye, goodbye." And we all started crying. And Kimo is part Hawaiian, he said "Aloha" and the other two of us said "Aloha" and the two men carried her into the morgue.

After Max stopped telling his story and you stopped recording, you thought of the news service photo of Jane's covered body being brought down the stairs on a stretcher. And you asked yourself *Who did she belong to then?* and you supposed that the medical examiner or the coroner would have said, "She's ours." And what of her parents?

And now, you think, she's Becky's. Truly, she's Becky's because Becky's bringing her back to life.

Up there you thought about death, including your own. Mostly you thought about how best to write about it, because in the novel you'd have Kate's death by murder, you'd have Desmond's death at Max's hands, and then— because you were pretty sure how it would end, you'd have Max's death or, as you imagined it, his disappearance on Mauna Loa.

In the end, you thought, Max would be unable to bear being a killer, although he'd had no problem with himself as Kate's avenger, which meant killing Desmond, or at least orchestrating his death.

Sometimes, up there in the koa forest with birdsong, or down in the eucalyptus with occasional wild pigs, you said to yourself *Too many variables* because you couldn't make yourself choose how Max engineered Desmond's death, and the ending depended on that.

Then you found another road that climbed even higher, through older forest. The road was very rough in places, which you liked. It broke your rhythm, which—surprisingly—pleased you. In the bad places, which were always steep, you had to pick your way, sometimes on pahoehoe lava, sometimes on loose stone, sometimes dirt or mud.

One day you climbed to the first small dam, the first ford, but didn't cross. You hadn't liked the look of Mauna Kea in the places it was visible, so you went down to the ford, took some pictures, and went back.

Another day when the mountain was clear, you crossed the river at the ford, went into a beautiful ōhiʻa and koa forest, forded another stream, then another, and finally the road ended. You had no idea at all that forests like that existed so close to Hilo. The only one like it you knew was miles away along Keanakolu Road, on Mauna Kea. You and Ruth had gone there many times, although not since the protests. You knew you would never go there again.

You took pictures and sent them to your son. There was more birdsong than you'd ever heard except at the volcano or on Mauna Kea. Some parts of the road were so beautiful your heart hurt the way it had, years before, high on Mauna Kea photographing silverswords and you found yourself on your knees at your tripod making a closeup in the rising sun and there was so much beauty that you wept. This road, not ten miles from your house, was as beautiful. Close quarters, no vistas. Only forest, grass, birds, sun. And a thirty-six inch iron water pipe running alongside the road. But that was all right. On that road the beauty was close to you. Intimate. The waterworks along the road, the same. At the end, another dam and beyond it a large grove of bananas. Whose were they? Wild? No way to know.

No matter how beautiful it was, you were always aware of danger. Sometimes you laughed, because by then you'd already written the first "Shibai" version that declared "you don't have to ford any rivers to get home," but now you're putting yourself in places where you do. There are three places where you could be cut off, and what then? Call for a helicopter rescue, and be ashamed, or burrow in the grass, spend the night, wait for the river to go down?

So you watched the mountain and didn't linger on the far side of the first ford. And—remembering Nagovisi rivers and the Wailuku's own quick fury—when you walked the widest ford, perhaps a tenth of a mile, you turned your head and looked upstream. Every time, as if a flood might arise from nothing and carry you away as the tsunami, itself humping up from the dark bay to pull at your legs and nearly take you, almost had. You couldn't help it.

Part of all this was because the river bed there at the first ford was like no river you'd ever seen, anywhere. The lower Wailuku is in a gorge. This was a plain, a lava plain, flat and no more than ten or fifteen feet down from the bank. You could imagine being swept into a channel in another part of the Wailuku and somehow hoisting yourself on a tree root, a log, anything but to be swept out along that lava plain would be like being carried out to sea, helpless.

Even so, you loved it there. You dropped all your other routes, except when you only had time for three or four miles. One day you wandered up top a half-marathon's worth. You didn't care about your time at all.

Sometimes, on that road, you spun around, walked backwards, arms out, sometimes face to the sky. It wasn't like Mauna Kea, where you'd been at home for years. It was a new place and therefore you did things you'd never done on Mauna Kea.

You knew you'd be leaving it. And you knew you'd never return. In your heart, that was the deal: when you go, you won't return.

Some days you sent pictures to Becky, some days you sent pictures to Ruth. One day Becky immediately sent pictures of where *she* was, on Boston Harbor.

*How did I not know about this place?* you asked yourself, and then, suddenly, it was time to pack the container.

Time to sell the 4Runner. No more Mauna Kea, even though the protestors had finally withdrawn.

Suddenly it was COVID-19 time, and the authorities began restricting access to Narnia itself, because large crowds sometimes congregated there on Sundays. And, as a guard said to you one day, "That's our water supply. We don't want the virus in it." You didn't think it worked that way, but you said nothing. The upper roads and the fords stayed open.

One Sunday you told the guard that you were a Hilo boy who was moving to the Mainland for good, and asked him for one more walk down to Narnia. "Go, brah," he said, "last time, yeah?" and you replied, "Last time."

You're coming down from Narnia, back on the public road. A big guy with an Idaho t-shirt is asking a local person walking his dog how to get to Narnia, but it looks like he's not getting the answer he wants. He holds up his hand and stops you. "How do I get to this Narnia place?" he asks.

You don't like his looks and you don't like his attitude. You can tell he's one of those know-it-all tourists who thinks locals are idiots. Everybody knows the type.

You tell him how to get there and then when you say the Wailuku can be dangerous he says "We have rivers where I come from," which pisses you off. You didn't like the look of the mountain when you were up there, but, pissed off or not, you don't want his death on your hands.

You take a step closer to him and say "Tell you something. You feel the current speeding up? See it's getting a little brown? Get the fuck out. Don't stop to think. Get the fuck up the nearest bank."

He looks surprised. Taken aback. A certain type of man's surprised when an old guy not only tells him what to do, but curses. You've never understood why.

OK. He's been warned. Fuck him if he dies.

After you leave him and are passing Boiling Pots you're remembering that the woman whose mother was waiting for her body had been trying to get back across the Wailuku after it started coming up. She and her compansion were afraid of getting stuck on the far side. He made it back across.

## APPROACHING THE FINISH LINE

IN WINTER, IT FEELS as though your three Jane years are winding down. What gathered around you in 2017 has loosened. There's not much pressure on you to be doing anything about Jane, which is good because you're under stress. You're fully committed to leaving Hilo, but that doesn't mean it's not difficult, even sometimes wrenching.

The container's on the ocean before the Ithaca house even closes. You're struggling with plane reservations. The airlines keep cancelling their long-haul flights out of Honolulu. You'll go to Ithaca first, and Ruth will follow. Somebody's got to be at the new place to meet the container. You tell Ruth how happy you'll be to live where you can drive anywhere you want to and aren't forced to fly.

The house remains unsold, which is a surprise but COVID-19 uncertainty and travel quarantines explain much of it. Your target markets were Honolulu, and even the mainland. But people can't get over to look at the place. You'd rather not leave with it unsold, but it looks as though you're going to have to.

Peter gets a major award and sends a picture of himself in his MSP uniform. He doesn't look comfortable in it, but that must be because it's not his working costume. Special occasions only. A few weeks later you email him, but the email bounces back. You think that means he's retired. You make a note to call him, but you don't get around to it. There's nothing much to talk about anyway, but you do miss knowing that he's out there and being able to reach him if you want to.

Becky's book is moving along, she tells you. Increasingly you're wanting to know how she's organizing it, but you don't ask. She tells you it's going to be a big book, which pleases you.

Your novel's fallowing, but you're not worried. Fallow is good. You'll pick it up after you settle into Ithaca. The only thing you're unhappy about is that you'd meant to go down to the courthouse and look at the transcript of a trial that now figures into the novel—another crime you're going to build on—but before you do, the courthouse closes to the public and you're out of luck.

You're thinking about rewriting and expanding "Shibai." Maybe you'll do that over the summer, or in the fall, a short project before resuming the novel. You read through the draft you sent out (which was rejected) thinking about what you might do with it, and when you get to the diming section you wonder, again, about the nature of that false accusation. What did they actually allege? So you ask for the file.

You're astonished. The boyfriend's is a mashup of what was in the 1969 news reports plus what a five-minute Google search might have turned up. There's literally nothing incriminating or even potentially incriminating there. How could he have thought this was tip-worthy?

For Mary's, you have the call-back detective's hand-written notes of the phone call Peter told you about. You see "Doesn't want name publicized," which makes you smile, but then another note catches your eye: "Mitch and wife kill Jane."

So. Mary actually accused you of killing Jane. At first you're pissed off, but then you shake your head and laugh, because there's not a single follow-up note. No details. Nothing. It's exactly as Peter told you: the tip line people immediately knew it was bullshit, and dropped it.

More shibai.

# MYSTERIES

IN THE SPRING, you and Becky were talking about Jane and you found that your perspective had shifted. When you began working with Becky, you thought you knew more about Jane than she did. You had seen Jane, touched her, talked to her, been close to her, and Becky had not.

But since spring 2017 Becky had been learning more and more about Jane and by winter 2020 she knew far more about her than you did. It's as if a graph of your "Jane knowledge" was a flat line, and hers inflected upward.

Becky told you that, in trying to get into Jane's head, she had actually typed all of Jane's letters rather than scanning them and reading them. You were astonished. What an strategy, especially to incorporate motion, movement. Hands on a keyboard, never mind that it was a MacBook rather than a typewriter (you couldn't remember what kind of typewriter Jane had, although Becky probably knew).

The idea of experiencing each word, each phrase through a completely different sensory suite was, you thought, genius. It made you want to go back to your old letters and try the same thing, in case it triggered memories you hadn't been able to recover.

You began wondering how much Becky knew about you, too. Of course you'd revealed yourself in many ways. You'd sent her things you'd written, she'd seen photos, the two of you had been together in person, she'd heard your voice and read what you'd written when you were elated, nervous (or frightened), or discouraged and even depressed. And there had been a continual stream of texts and emails, more rarely phone calls. There's nothing surprising about that.

The surprise came when you realized that because Becky had the case files, all the interviews and other observations about you, she was learning more and more about you, but not from you—at least not from you in the modern era. You didn't remember everything you said to the cops, and what they said to you. *Every bad thing* was clearly in your memory, as was *We know you were fucking her,* and the flayed skull with its *Did you do this?* but how bad or dumb or out of it did you seem in those transcripts?

You wanted to see them, remembering what you'd had Elliot write about his journal and notes, "When he goes to those pages twenty, thirty years in the future, confronting himself represented by himself, will he recognize the contortions of his *I?*" Except in those transcripts you'd be represented by the police as well as what other people said of you.

You had no fear of what might emerge from the case files, and you had no fear that Becky would use them in a way that would be hurtful. In fact you knew that if she did, you'd be all right with it, even admire her courage. You wouldn't think of it as betrayal. And back you go to the beginning when, even without knowing her, you told her you were all in. And you've never faltered, never changed your mind.

Still, you hope there's nothing in there that makes you look bad. And "bad" covers a lot of territory.

In March, you spend several pleasant hours on Skype with Sameen Gauhar, Becky's fact-checker. You'd never been fact-checked before and although you weren't worried about anything, you wondered how it would go—how it would be done, how the facts would be presented to you, not to mention the nature of the facts themselves. Because Sameen was skillful and the two of you were effectively face-to-face, it went easily. And was fascinating.

You hadn't thought that you'd need to assess what you'd said to the detectives, but as soon as Sameen began going over the transcripts it became obvious. Had the detectives or the transcribers distorted what you'd said? Or had Becky in some way accidentally distorted it? You came to understand that this sort of fact-checking was less *Is this true?* than *Has this been accurately reported?* It made perfect sense, but it wasn't what you'd been expecting.

The difficulty was when you had to judge the accuracy of something the transcript reported you'd said, but you couldn't remember having said it. Talk about Elliot's *Contortions of the I*, or better here, *Contortions of the you*—did it sound like something you might have said? Did it seem like a different thing you might have said that was mis-reported by the detectives? Sometimes you couldn't get anywhere, and defaulted to telling Sameen that if it was in the transcript, you must have said it.

These problems were more interesting than troublesome. You remembered that Peter had talked about how the recordings had gone from reel-to-reel tape to cassettes and finally to digital media. When you'd done the same thing with your Nagovisi recordings from a half-century ago you'd learned that inevitably there were dropouts and distortions and lots of noise, both electronic and ambient. You hadn't asked Becky whether what she had was transcribed from the final media, or were transcripts from the early tapes.

And, you thought, here's Elliot again "adding comments and thoughts that occur to him while he types, piling on another layer of interpretation, amplifying and distancing himself and the journal still farther from the events of the day."

You assume the stenographer didn't do this, but you know from Peter on Mauna Kea that the detectives added notes and comments, some of them unflattering, even nasty (but not about you). If Becky didn't have the originals, she wouldn't have seen those, which seemed a pity.

But wait—if Peter had seen the comments, that meant that the original transcriptions still existed. And because you can't imagine that the DA's office would want to pay for new transcriptions of the preserved recordings, that must mean Becky had seen the originals which, in your view, was the best possible situation.

But what if you said something that wasn't recorded or transcribed accurately and a detective had written a comment, wouldn't that mean that the comment was invalid? How would Becky know whether the transcription was accurate if you couldn't remember having said it?

The whole business was a swamp, but an amusing one, because nothing was at stake.

At least not until Sameen quoted you: "Jill said if anything should happen to her, you should marry Jane because she'd always been in love with you." That was a shock. You had only a vague memory of that, but you told Sameen that if it was in the transcript, you must have said it.

*Was Jane in love with me?* you asked yourself, and you had no answer beyond what you said more than fifty years ago. Over the years you'd never wondered about that.

You finished your work with Sameen and put the Jane question aside for later, because it was crunch time for your move to Ithaca. You didn't return to that question until May, when you were already in Ithaca.

Becky sent a picture of Jane and two other graduate students, outside, standing next to a car. Jane's wearing a wild print dress that you remember. She's wearing dark glasses, smiling, but not looking at the camera.

Becky wrote, "It's amazing how much more shy she looks in this photo than in the ones you took," and that hurled you back to what Sameen had asked, back to the portrait sessions, where you'd felt as if the two of you were dancing. Where you'd felt something flowing between you. Shy? But not shy with you?

So. Did she love you? And you completely missed it? You'd told Becky countless times that you'd loved Jane, but you'd meant love of a friend you cared deeply for, although you never denied the sexual undercurrents. But they weren't what it was about.

You asked Becky whether there was anything in Jane's letters, her papers, suggesting love for you? She said there wasn't.

Whether what you reported to the detectives was accurate or not didn't matter. What mattered to you, sitting in a sparsely-furnished house in Ithaca waiting for Ruth to make her way from Hilo, was something more distressing. You texted Becky that you were

wrestling with how I failed (in modern times) to consider anything from Jane's POV. And this

250

hurts, because I think I'm good at going beyond my own perspective and try to enter others'…it was all Jane-as-perceived-by-Don. Not my usual mode but it surely was, has been, the case with JSB. So that's part of what's bothering me—not that I did or didn't do anything half a century ago, but when thinking about how Jane and I were connected, doing that thinking in the present, I really blew it.

Becky responded

…don't be so hard on yourself. We're all stuck in our own version of events, or of people, and our perception of them. Maybe the important part is that you're thinking about it now. As a wise writer once wrote, 'what looked like impenetrable forest that I didn't even recognize, much less think about entering, is now semi-open country with interesting new trails running through it'

You didn't realize for some time that she'd quoted your own words to you. Wise writer, indeed. Interesting new trails, indeed.

Something opened up in you. You began to take seriously the notion that Jane *saw you for what you were*, that you were not the anonymous spectator you'd been making yourself, both director and audience in your own shibai.

If you can imagine yourself as visible to someone but her vision is opaque to you, as Jane's is, what's left for you is to make yourself visible to yourself.

And that may explain why you've been trying to write this for three years, in second person. What you've been attempting to understand about Jane has been perhaps more about your trying to understand yourself.

*It's a mystery*, you say to yourself, and sitting in your workroom and looking out at the forest returns you to Nagovisi, 1969. You were sitting with the missionary priest, a New Zealander, in his house, a different forest out the window, drinking his Johnny Walker whiskey.

You'd been thinking about the Assumption of Mary into Heaven, because in the tracts scattered around his house you'd read that it was one of the "Mysteries."

You asked the priest whether there was theology that explains or untangles the Mysteries and he said, surprising you, "We don't try to figure them out. They are Mysteries and they stay mysteries. That's their nature."

You'd been thinking of theologians as spiritual detectives, perpetually trying to figure out their supernatural world, as you were trying to figure out the Nagovisi's, but you didn't say that.

Becky's done the detective work and come up empty. There's no evidence. Better there is none, nothing to interpret or parse or unpack. Better to go with the priest's take. Better for what Jane felt about you to remain a mystery.

# CATWALK

YOUR ITHACA PROPERTY has trails all through the forest. Paul, who sold you the house, told you that when his daughter was a little girl, he laid out the trails so that no matter what turn she took, she always ended up back at the house. As long as she stayed on a trail—any trail—she would never get lost, no matter how far down the ridge or into the forest the trail looped.

After you settled in, you and Ruth and the cats would go walking on the cleared trails and when you saw what looked like an overgrown trail heading off somewhere, into what sometimes looked like impenetrable bush, you returned and cut the brush with the machete you had in Nagovisi, now fifty-two years old, your name carved on the handle, and you swung your new Home Depot axe when it was needed to open the trail. Then you brought the small tractor and mowed it.

Sure enough, every overgrown trail you and Ruth cleared looped back to another one. Some ran through the pines, some through stands of maple, some in trees you couldn't identify, some went through thickets of blackberries and raspberries, some ran around the edges of the large wildflower beds that were in their last year and you knew

253

you'd have to mow down, till, and replant. An apple tree, goldenrod, thistles, an asparagus bed. Stands of milkweed. Bees, butterflies, and, sad to say, deer flies, black flies, wasps, and ticks. Dozens of deer. A red fox, a fisher. Sometimes coyotes; Paul told you about a bear. Hawks, owls, turkey vultures. Hummingbirds.

'Ōhi'a, your beloved tortoiseshell cat, hunted in the wildflower beds and in the woods but, one day, was taken by a predator. Perhaps the fox, perhaps a hawk, perhaps the fisher, who broke into Paul's chicken coop and killed all his chickens one night not long before you arrived.

All you know is that at five one morning, as was your habit, you walked out into the woods with her and the other cat, Pippin, sent them on their way to be cats in the woods, and only Pippin returned. You and Pippin walked the woods, looking for bits of fur, maybe bones, broke open scat, but found nothing.

This was the first sorrow on your ridge and you marked it not by planting trees, but by planting a rugosa rose for 'Ōhi'a in the hard stony soil of the wildflower bed. Rugosa are badass roses. Although 'Ōhi'a was a sweet cat—though braver than was safe for her—it seemed to you and Ruth that an ordinary rose, even a beautiful heirloom one, would be too sentimental. Rugosa will grow five or six feet tall, wide and thick with roses and thorns.

Of course you thought of Jane and her Hilo 'ōhi'a, and how you'd chosen a badass one for her. Of course you thought of Becky's 'ōhi'a, a striking red one that grew faster and taller and made more blossoms than all the others. Both 'ōhi'a, thousands of miles away, are lost to you now.

One morning when you were nearly finished with this book you put your phone in your pocket and went out to walk the trails. You had in your head a few questions you wanted to chew on and you didn't feel like sitting at your computer and typing. You circled around to where you'd last seen ʻŌhiʻa and called to her even though she'd been gone for weeks, which brought Pippin out of the forest to join you.

You walked with your cat and spoke into your phone.

> I have to somehow answer the question of why did this stay with me for all these years? Why? Because a person might argue, all right, this is a terrible event, your friend was murdered, you were treated badly, but that kind of stuff happens to a lot of people, say a car accident. A horrible event that remains in some way unresolved, like why did the other car cross the center line, maybe that's constantly on a person's mind for years.

> But you know, it's not your mother who died, not your sister, not your partner, your father, whatever, it's a good friend. So I gotta work on that because some people are gonna think that's different and I shouldn't have *just a friend* on my mind for fifty years.

> What I think at the moment is that it stayed with me because of the unsolved thing and the wrongness of it. Yes, everybody who gets killed is wronged, but a person who had so much potential, that I admired in so many ways...but that's weak, you know, that's not much of anything. It's just saying,

Oh, a horrible thing happened to somebody that you cared about and you couldn't let go of it. So that's really the last piece. I have to deal with that. Why? Why so strong?

Because it just is, that's all. Why should I have to defend it? It's nobody's business who I mourn and for how long.

I'm walking and Pips is doing the thing cats always do. It might be good to write about that and liken having a cat along with you on a walk to this whole Jane thing. Namely Pips'll disappear into the bushes, and then he comes rocketing up from behind and passes me, maybe stops for a second, but usually doesn't. He goes rocketing ahead and disappears into the forest, until I've passed him again, classic cat stuff, but that would be perhaps a way to end it actually, saying here in Ithaca, in my woods and my wildflower beds and my interlocking trails, I go walking with my cat. And most of the time I don't see him but I know he's there and I know he's watching me.

And perhaps I can put it to rest by saying, well, that's just the way it is. A catwalk. Except. Except Jane's not a cat. The case isn't like a cat. Except it is. They are. Saying so doesn't diminish them.

I mowed down the wildflower beds last week. So they're ready for replanting and I'm going to till them pretty soon if I can get the big tractor started.

Well, maybe in some way, this whole three years have been a matter of walking with a cat. And finally I'm okay, thanks to Becky and Ruth, Peter and the others. I've mowed everything down. It's clear.

So maybe now, when I walk with my cat, as I am this very minute, he's simply a companion who's playing and hiding and this isn't an analogy for anything. It's just my cat going for a walk in my woods.

Oh, here I am at 'Ōhi'a's rugosa. I was just looking at Pippin and thinking about 'Ōhi'a. Something to work in at the end, you know, we are in a new place now and we've lost a beloved companion to a predator.

You can't, no one would compare the loss of a cat to the loss of a human being. A cat is not a human being, that's true, but the heart doesn't know the difference.

Goodbye, Jane. Aloha.

# ACKNOWLEDGMENTS

I thank Becky Cooper, without whom this book would not exist, Ruth Thompson, who not only pushed me to write it, but read what must have seemed to her endless drafts, and Irving Feldman, whose friendship and wise counsel guided me though the rough parts.

Opal Greer's reading of the earlier, short versions was tremendously helpful. Other readers of the various earlier versions included Sean Beaudoin, Ronlyn Domingue, Stefan Kiesbye, Ginia Loo, and ire'ne lara silva. I'm grateful to all of them.

I'm greatly indebted to Boyd Britton, Alyssa Bertetto, Todd Wallack, and Michael Widmer.

Detective Sergeant Peter Sennott, Massachusetts State Police, not only cracked the case, but became a friend on whom I could rely. Thank you, Peter.

Dennis Knuckles, Bobby Camara, and Chris King helped with the Mauna Loa information. I hope to be thanking them again in *Excavation*, the novel mentioned in this book.

Information about EnVision Maunakea (and the Report mentioned) can be found at envisionmaunakea. org.

"Ever After" is reprinted from *Collected Poems 1954-2004* by Irving Feldman. Schocken Books, 2004. By permission.

The Bach piece mentioned in "Planting the 'Ōhi'a" is the Toccata from his Toccata and Fugue in F Major, BWV 540. The version I prefer is Michael Murray's (Telarc 2022804).

The multimedia piece "Queen of the Night" can be found on YouTube by searching for "Queen of the Night Don Mitchell."

A note about collaboration: Becky Cooper and I were each generally aware of what the other was doing, but I saw nothing of *We Keep The Dead Close* until after I completed work on *Shibai* in late October, 2020.

## About Don Mitchell

Don Mitchell is an ecological anthropologist, writer, book designer, and photographer. He grew up in Hilo, on the island of Hawai'i, and graduated from Hilo High School. He studied anthropology, evolutionary biology, and creative writing at Stanford and earned a Ph.D. in anthropology from Harvard.

He lived among the Nagovisi people of Bougainville for several years in the 1960s and 1970s, and returned briefly in 2001 after Bougainville's war of secession.

For many years he was a professor of anthropology at Buffalo State, a unit of the State University of New York.

In his non-academic life, he was a dedicated marathon and ultra-marathon runner and a professional road race timer (operating for 25 years as Runtime Services). He continues to tackle long distances on foot, though much more slowly.

He lived in Buffalo and later in Colden, New York, where he and the poet Ruth Thompson lived before they returned to his childhood home in Hilo. In mid-2020 they left Hilo for Ithaca, New York.

He published an academic book and articles about Nagovisi, but in the early 1990s returned to writing fiction and poetry. His stories have won praise from many quarters, including a Pushcart nomination and awards from the Society for Humanistic Anthropology, *New Millennium Writings* and other journals.

His photographs have won competitions and have hung in several Hawai'i galleries.

He designs books for several small publishers.

He has been an Artist in Residence for the City of Portales, New Mexico, and in 2019 shared (with Ruth Thompson) the Jack Williamson Visiting Professor of English Chair at Eastern New Mexico University.

In Hawai'i, he was actively involved in matters concerning Mauna Kea, Hawai'i's tallest and most contested mountain.

CPSIA information can be obtained
at www.ICGtesting.com
Printed in the USA
LVHW112239170821
695543LV00019B/416